math INNOVATIONS

COURSE 1

MOVING MATH FORWARD THROUGH CRITICAL THINKING AND EXPLORATION

A Balancing Act

Focusing on Equality, Algebraic Expressions and Equations

Linda Jensen Sheffield

Suzanne H. Chapin

M. Katherine Gavin

Kendall Hunt
publishing company

ACKNOWLEDGMENTS

Math Innovations Writing Team

Authors
Linda Jensen Sheffield
Suzanne H. Chapin
M. Katherine Gavin

Project Manager
Janice M. Vuolo

Teacher Edition Team
Alice J. Gabbard
Jennifer M. MacPherson
Ann Marie Spinelli

Writing Assistants
Jane Paulin
Jacob J. Whitmore
Kathy Dorkin

Mathematics Editor
Kathleen G. Snook

Assessment Specialist
Nancy Anderson

Advisory Board
Jerry P. Becker
Janet Beissinger
Diane J. Briars
Ann Lawrence
Ira J. Papick

Kendall Hunt
publishing company

www.kendallhunt.com
Send all inquiries to:
4050 Westmark Drive
Dubuque, IA 52004-1840
1-800-542-6657

ISBN 978-0-7575-6212-9

Production Date: 12/28/12
Printed by: One TouchPoint-CCI
Hartland, Wisconsin
United States of America
Batch number: 42621203

Printed in the United States of America
4 5 6 7 8 9 10   13 12 11 10 09

A Balancing Act:
Focusing on Equality, Algebraic Expressions and Equations
Table of Contents

UNIT GOALS

A Balancing Act: Focusing on Equality, Algebraic Expressions and Equations

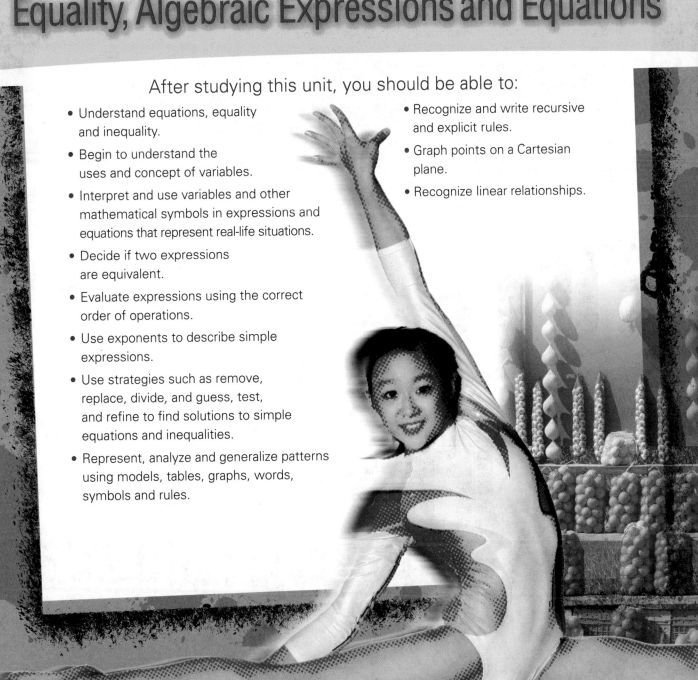

After studying this unit, you should be able to:

- Understand equations, equality and inequality.
- Begin to understand the uses and concept of variables.
- Interpret and use variables and other mathematical symbols in expressions and equations that represent real-life situations.
- Decide if two expressions are equivalent.
- Evaluate expressions using the correct order of operations.
- Use exponents to describe simple expressions.
- Use strategies such as remove, replace, divide, and guess, test, and refine to find solutions to simple equations and inequalities.
- Represent, analyze and generalize patterns using models, tables, graphs, words, symbols and rules.

- Recognize and write recursive and explicit rules.
- Graph points on a Cartesian plane.
- Recognize linear relationships.

Dear Student Mathematician,

When you think about mathematics, do you think about numbers and operations like addition, subtraction, multiplication, and division? Do you also think about patterns, logic, order, and beauty in the world around you? Thinking of mathematics as just the study of numbers is like thinking of science as just the study of plants and animals. There is more to mathematics than just numbers!

In this unit, you will experience a broader view of mathematics. We hope that you will learn to think like a mathematician—making sense of mathematical concepts, searching for patterns, and using mathematics to discover the world around you. You will journey around the world and through history as you explore mathematics through the eyes of such influential thinkers as Galileo, who said, "Nature's great book is written in mathematics," and Descartes, who said, "Mathematics is a more powerful instrument of knowledge than any other." The goal will not be for you just to learn what they knew, but rather for you to develop your own understanding and make your own new discoveries.

In this unit, you will begin to think like a mathematician using concepts of number, symbols, and equality. We will start with Pythagoras, who is known as the "father of numbers," and his wife, Theano, who was also a mathematician. Over 2500 years ago in Greece, the men and women who followed Pythagoras and Theano, known as the Pythagorean Society, believed that everything was related to mathematics, and that mathematics could be used to predict and measure the patterns of the world.

By reading, writing, and understanding mathematics, you will discover the power of algebra. Algebra allows us to use symbols to show the general concepts, properties, and rules that you have previously used with specific numbers in arithmetic.

As famed scientist Marie Curie said, "Nothing in life is to be feared, it is only to be understood." We hope you will enjoy this journey.

Mathematically yours,
The Authors

Linda Sheffield

Suzanne H. Chapin

M. Katherine Gavin

Making Sense of Equality

When you think like a mathematician, you use mathematics to make sense of the world. Every human brain is designed to look for patterns. You will use patterns in your mathematical investigations to solve problems with balance, equality and equations.

LESSON 1.1 A Balancing Act: Understanding Equivalence and Patterns

 Start It Off

The following table lists the results of multiplying the one-digit counting numbers by 9.

First Factor	Second Factor	Product
9	1	9
9	2	18
9	3	27
9	4	36
9	5	45
9	6	54
9	7	63
9	8	72
9	9	81

1. List at least three patterns you notice. Look for patterns within each column and across all three columns.

2. Test whether your patterns hold when you multiply 9 by a two-digit number. Use several examples.

The ancient Greeks, Pythagoras, Theano and the other Pythagoreans believed that mathematics is the key to understanding the universe. They believed that the study of patterns is essential to all mathematics. They saw patterns in everyday objects that could be touched and counted. This grew to abstract concepts of numbers and patterns that existed only in the mind. We will start as the Pythagoreans did, using concrete objects and studying patterns.

For centuries, scales and balances have been used to weigh things. Look at the balance below. Note that the two sides are in balance when the weight of the objects on one side is equal to the weight of the objects on the other side.

MATHEMATICALLY SPEAKING

▶ equal

In the time of Pythagoras, scales and balances were often used to find the weight of coins to make sure trades were fair. The value of a coin was determined by its weight and the type of metal it was made from. For example, a silver stater weighed twice as much as a silver half-stater and was also worth twice as much. Other coins used in ancient Greece were trites, hektes, drachms and obols.

Example

Helena has Scale A below in front of her. She wants to know how many trites are needed to equal the value of one stater. What should she do? On one side she sees two staters (S). This balances with one stater and three trites (T). Helena removed a stater from each side to find the weight of a stater. Using this "remove" strategy, she found that one stater had the same weight as three trites.

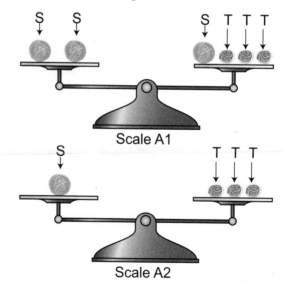

Scale A1

Scale A2

Helena saw on Scale B that three trites also weighed the same as another coin she had, a tetradrachm (Te). She wondered how the weight of a tetradachm compared to the weight of a stater. She knew from Scale A that three trites had the same weight as one stater. So, she replaced the three trites on the right with one stater. Using this "replace" strategy, Helena found that one stater had the same weight as one tetradrachm.

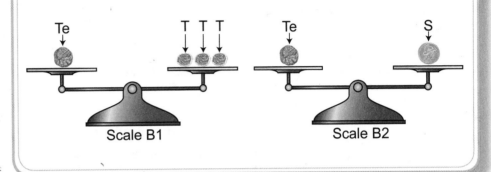

Scale B1   Scale B2

Use the strategies of remove and replace to solve the following coin problems about the coins from ancient Greece.

1. Alexander could find the value of staters (S), hektes (H), obols (O), and drachm (D) coins using the scales below.

   a) What might Alexander use to balance the two hektes on Scale E? Can he balance the scale with one coin? How can you use the strategies of remove and replace to solve this problem?

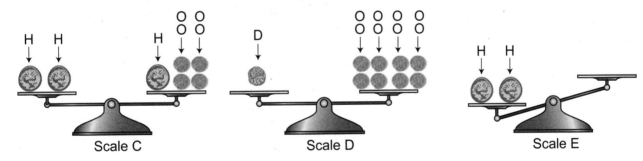

Scale C   Scale D   Scale E

   b) Use what you learned about the weights of the coins in Part a to determine how many hektes it would take to balance the stater on Scale G below. Explain how you found your answer.

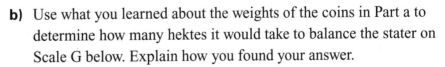
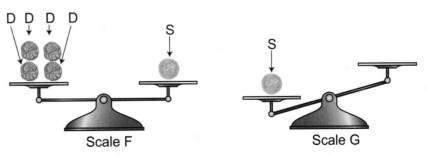

Scale F   Scale G

Jake decided to make up his own coin puzzles for Questions 2–4. His coins were named after the animals shown on them: pigs (P), rabbits (R), turkeys (T), goats (G), frogs (F), monkeys (M) and bats (B). All coins with the same animal weigh the same.

2. Use Scales H–I to find the number of rabbit coins it would take to balance a turkey coin. Explain how you solved this.

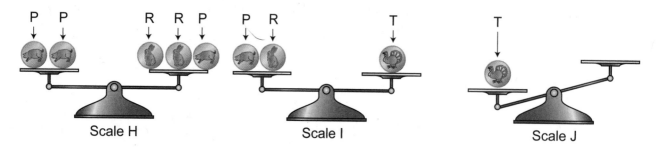

3. How many frog coins would you need to put on the right side of Scale M? Discuss the strategies you used with a partner.

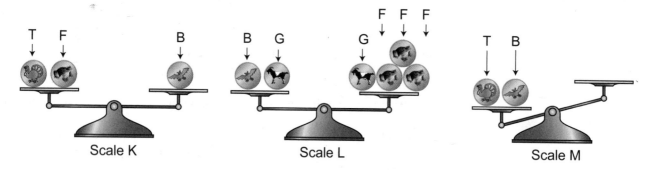

4. a) What coins might you put on the right side of Scale P to balance it? Explain.

   b) Is there another way you might do this? Compare your answer to a partner's.

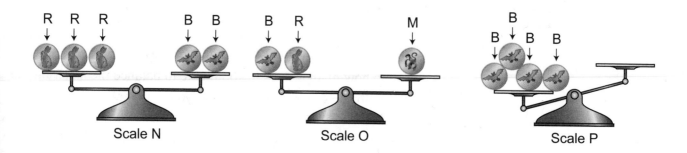

Brody and Jake found an old scale at home and decided to weigh fruit. They found that all fruit of the same type weighed the same.

5. Look at Scale Q. The weight of the two apples is the same as the weight of one banana and one pear.

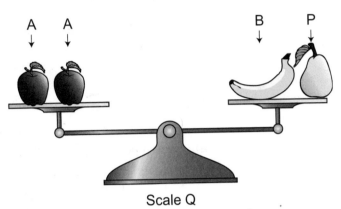

Scale Q

a) If each apple weighs 4 ounces, list at least five possible pairs of weights for the banana and the pear. Use a chart like the one below.

Banana	Pear

b) What patterns do you notice on your chart?

c) If each fruit weighs a whole number of ounces, how many pairs of weights are possible for the banana and the pear?

d) If the fruit could weigh a fractional number of ounces, how many pairs of weights are possible?

e) Suppose you know the weight of one apple and the banana. How would you find the weight of the pear? Is there more than one correct answer?

f) If you know the weight of the pear and the banana, how would you find the weight of three apples?

6. Use Scale R to answer the questions below. Note that all fruits of the same type will have the same weight. (Since this is a new problem, the weights might be different than in other problems.)

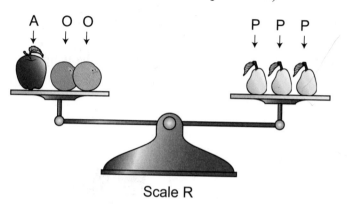

Scale R

a) If each pear weighs 5 ounces, give at least five possible pairs of weights for each apple and orange. Use a chart like the one below.

Apple	Orange

b) What patterns do you notice on this chart?

c) If one apple weighs 3 ounces and one pear weighs 4 ounces, what is the weight of one orange? Is there more than one correct answer?

d) If you know the weight of one apple and one orange, how can you find the weight of one pear? Is there more than one correct answer?

e) If you know the weight of one pear and one orange, how can you find the weight of three apples? Is there more than one correct answer?

f) If the weights of two types of fruit are given, is there a single answer for the weight of the third type of fruit?

g) If the weight of one type of fruit is given, is there a single answer for the weights of the other two types of fruit?

7. **a)** Make up a balance puzzle that has a single correct answer. Trade puzzles with a partner and solve. Compare answers.

b) Make up a balance puzzle that has many possible answers and trade with a partner. If you have a different answer than your partner, is each answer correct? How do you know? If you have the same answers, see whether you can find others.

⬆ Wrap It Up

MATHEMATICALLY SPEAKING

▶ equal

Explain how you solve balance puzzles using the strategies of remove and replace. Use the Scales S-U below in your explanation. Same shapes have the same weight. How many cubes will balance the three pyramids?

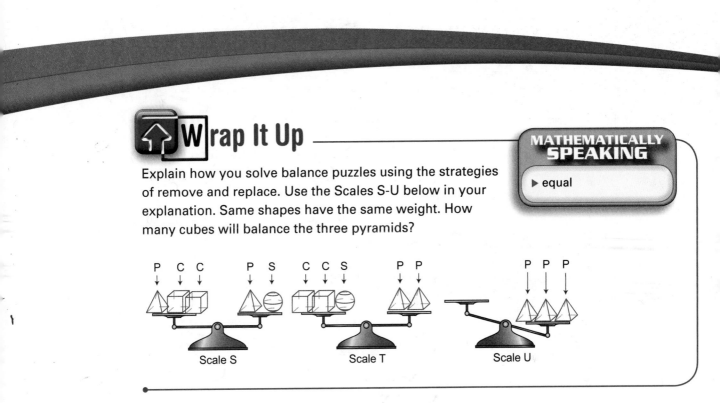

Scale S Scale T Scale U

LESSON
1.1

SECTION 1

On Your Own

MATERIALS LIST

▶ Lesson Guide 1.1A
(optional)

**Write About It**

1. In the following balance puzzle, fruits of the same type have the same weight. How many cherries does it take to balance a plum? Use "remove" and "replace" in your explanation.

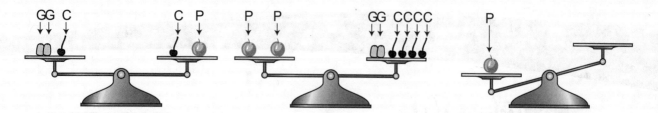

2. Ms. Martines bought several types of cheese for a party: American cheese (A), cheddar cheese (C) and Swiss cheese (S). All packages of the same type of cheese weigh the same. How many packages of American cheese would it take to balance one package of Swiss cheese?

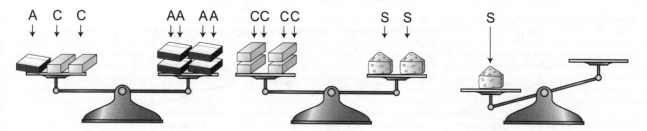

3. In the book *1001 Arabian Nights*, one of the most popular stories is "Aladdin." Imagine that Aladdin uses scales to weigh the diamonds (D), rubies (R) and emeralds (E) he finds. All jewels of the same type have the same weight.

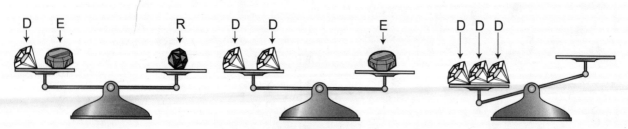

   a) What single jewel balances three diamonds?

   b) What combination of jewels could balance three diamonds?

   c) If the diamond weighs 4 grams, can the emerald weigh 10 grams? Explain.

   d) If the diamond weighs 4 grams, what is the weight of the ruby? Is there more than one correct answer? Explain.

4. Aladdin has found pearls (P) that each weigh 3 grams.

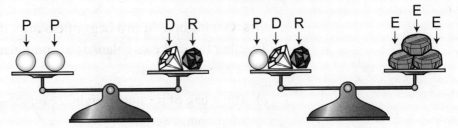

a) What do the diamond and the ruby weigh together?

b) What is the weight of one emerald? Is there more than one correct answer?

c) List at least five different possible weights for one diamond and one ruby.

Diamond	Ruby

d) What patterns do you notice in the weights of one diamond and one ruby?

e) Make a chart listing three different ways that you can balance the four emeralds using diamonds, pearls and/or rubies.

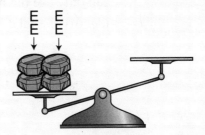

5. Marisol loves to fish. She caught two trout, each of the same size, and one catfish. Each trout weighs $1\frac{1}{2}$ pounds. Together all the fish weigh 6 pounds. How much does the catfish weigh?

6. Mrs. Collins bought two bags of cashews that weigh 3 ounces each. Together the cashews balance the combined weight of a bag of peanuts and a bag of almonds.

a) If the bag of peanuts weighs $2\frac{3}{4}$ ounces, how much does the bag of almonds weigh?

b) Make a chart to show three different combinations of weights for the bag of peanuts and the bag of almonds.

Think Beyond

7. When Sue and her father get on the scale together, they find that they weigh the same amount as when her older brother John gets on the scale with their mother. John's father weighs 180 pounds and when he gets on the scale with his wife, the total is 300 pounds. John weighs four times as much as Sue. How much does John weigh? Show your reasoning.

Think Beyond

8. Balance puzzles are seen around the world. Work through these questions.

a) Jameel has a scale and nine coins. All nine of the coins look alike. Eight of the coins are real gold and have the same weight. The ninth coin is a fake and is heavier than the other coins. Jameel tells you that if you can identify the fake coin, then you get to keep all of the coins. However, you can only use the balance scale at most two times. How might you identify the fake coin?

b) Erin also has nine coins that look identical. Eight of the coins are real gold and have the same weight. The ninth coin is a fake, but you do not know whether it is lighter or heavier than the real coins. If you find the fake, you get to keep all the coins. However, you can only use the balance scale at most three times. How might you identify the fake coin?

9. Compute each of the following without a calculator. Show your work.

a) $45 \cdot 18 =$

b) $125 \div 34 =$

c) $2.45 + 8.2 + 0.97 =$

d) $20.08 - 2.79 =$

10. Fill in three more terms in each number list below. Explain the pattern you used.

a) 1, 2, 4, 8, _____ , _____ , _____

b) 1, 2, 4, 7, _____ , _____ , _____

c) 64, 32, 16, 8, _____ , _____ , _____

d) $3, 3\frac{1}{2}, 4, 4\frac{1}{2},$ _____ , _____ , _____

11. If you know that $47 + 52$ is equal to some number plus 49, how would you find the missing number?

12. Complete the following:

a) 1 pint = _____ cups

b) 1 yard = _____ inches

c) 1 meter = _____ centimeters

d) 1 mile = _____ feet

13. What is the probability of rolling a prime number on a number cube with sides labeled 1, 2, 3, 4, 5 and 6?

Representing Balance with Scales, Bars and Equations

→ Start It Off

There are 100 single-digit multiplication facts. The fact with the smallest product is $0 \cdot 0 = 0$ and the fact with the largest product is $9 \cdot 9 = 81$. Dan knows his basic facts through the fives. He also knows all the nines facts and understands the commutative property of multiplication for whole numbers. It states that you can switch the order of the factors and not change their product. So if you know $4 \cdot 7 = 28$, you also know $7 \cdot 4 = 28$.

1. How many facts must Dan still learn? List them.

2. List three tips you might give Dan to learn the facts you listed.

3. Does the commutative property also work for addition, subtraction or division of whole numbers? Explain.

MATHEMATICALLY SPEAKING

▶ commutative property of multiplication

▶ variable

Thousands of years ago, people around the world began to realize they could use numbers and other symbols to record many of the things they did. Some of the symbols stood for operations like addition or multiplication. Other symbols were variables, which are letters or other symbols that stand for a number or set of numbers. One of the most famous early mathematical records is the Rhind papyrus from Egypt, which is over 3,700 years old. This is a mathematical record of many things from everyday Egyptian life.

A Fish Story:
Using Variables, Expressions and Equations

Fish from the Nile were a big part of the Egyptian diet. Imagine Amal working in a fish market, keeping records. Amal could use variables, expressions and equations for his record keeping. An **expression** is a mathematical phrase made up of numbers, variables and/or operations. For example, Amal might use the variable n to stand for the weight of a swordfish in pounds. If a tuna weighs 13 pounds more than a swordfish, he might use the expression, $n + 13$ to represent the weight of the tuna.

1. The variable n stands for the weight of a swordfish in pounds. Match the expression in Column A with the words in Column B. Discuss your results with a partner.

Column A	Column B
a) $150n$	**i)** the weight of a tuna if the tuna and the swordfish together weigh 150 pounds
b) $n + 150$	**ii)** the number of swordfish if each one weighs n pounds and together they weigh 150 pounds
c) $150 - n$	**iii)** the weight of 150 swordfish that each weighs n pounds
d) $150 \div n$	**iv)** the weight of a tuna that weighs 150 pounds more than the swordfish

When two expressions have the same value, you can write an **equation**. An equation is a mathematical sentence with an equal sign. An equation shows that the expressions on the two sides of the equal sign have the same value.

Solving Equations Using a Balance

Amal has three fish that weigh 12 pounds, 13 pounds and 23 pounds. Amal will use a balance and these three fish to find the weight of a fourth fish. Look at the fish on the balance below. Using the variable n to stand for the unknown weight in pounds, Amal can write the equation $12 + 23 = 13 + n$.

When you solve an equation, you find a value that makes the equation true. This value is called the solution of the equation.

2. a) Write an equation for the weights of the fish on the scale below. Use n in your equation for the unknown weight in pounds.

b) Solve your equation for the missing weight. How might you do this without finding the total weight of the fish on the left side?

3. What value for n makes $12 + 23 = 13 + n$ a true statement? How might you determine this answer by thinking about balance and equality without using a pencil and paper or a calculator? How does your method relate to the balance scale?

4. a) Write an equation for the weights of the fish on the scale below. Use n in your equation for the unknown weight in pounds.

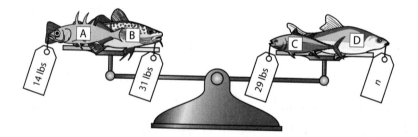

b) Solve your equation for the missing weight. Explain how you could find this weight without using a pencil and paper or a calculator.

5. a) Write an equation for the weights of the fish on the scale below. Use n in your equation for the unknown weight in pounds.

b) Solve your equation for the missing weight. Explain your reasoning to a partner.

Solving Equations Using Bar Diagrams

MATHEMATICALLY SPEAKING

▶ bar diagram

Mei Ling, who had attended school in Singapore, showed the class a different way to solve these problems. She used bar diagrams. To solve Question 2, Mei Ling drew the following bar diagram. Because the total weight on the left side of the scale is the same as the total weight on the right, she drew the bars for the two sides with the same length to show that the weights were equal. She also knew that 13 pounds is a little more than 12 pounds, so she made the 13-pound section of the bottom bar longer than the 12-pound section of the top bar.

12 pounds	23 pounds
13 pounds	n pounds

6. Explain how Mei Ling might find the weight of the fourth fish using her diagram.

7. Draw a bar diagram to solve the fish problem in Question 4 or Question 5. Show how you use the diagram to find the missing weight.

8. Bar diagrams can also be used for other problems. For the problems below, draw a bar diagram. Explain what the variable stands for. Then write an equation and solve for the variable.

   a) Jerra's age plus her mother's age is the same as Jason's age plus his father's age. Jerra is 12, Jason is 11 and Jason's father is 42. How old is Jerra's mother?

   b) Notebooks cost $2.95 each and two pens cost $1.95. A set of colored pencils and four pens have the same cost as three notebooks. How much does the set of colored pencils cost?

In each of the following equations, the variable *n* is used to stand for a missing number. This is similar to representing the unknown weights of the fish above. For each equation, try to find the value of *n* just by reasoning about balance and equality. Draw a balance or bar diagram if it helps you. Be prepared to explain your reasoning.

9. $4832 + 197 = n + 200$

10. $49 + n = 73 + 50$

11. $23 + n = 14 + 24$

12. $51 - n = 50 - 25$

13. $78 + 32 = 80 + n$

rap It Up

How does the equation $23 + n = 18 + 22$ relate to balance scales and bar diagrams? Sketch a balance scale and a bar diagram to show this. Explain how you would solve this problem without using pencil and paper or a calculator. What is the meaning of the *n* in this equation?

MATHEMATICALLY SPEAKING

▶ bar diagram

▶ commutative property of multiplication

▶ equation

▶ expression

▶ solution

▶ solve (an equation)

▶ variable

Write About It

1. **a)** Solve for n by reasoning about balance and equality without using a diagram. $n + 19 = 20 + 82$. Explain your method.

   b) Explain how to solve the same equation using a bar diagram and then using a balance scale.

2. For each of the following, the variable a stands for the number of apples in a crate. Column A describes the number of oranges in a crate. Match each expression in Column A with the words in Column B.

Column A	Column B
a) $3a$	**i)** The number of oranges in a crate is three more than the number of apples in a crate.
b) $a + 3$	**ii)** There are three times as many oranges in a crate as apples.
c) $a - 3$	**iii)** There are three more apples in the crate than oranges.
d) $a \div 3$	**iv)** There are one-third as many oranges in a crate as apples.

3. For each balance, write an equation. The first equation is written for you. Solve each equation for the unknown weight.

A = Antonio	85 pounds
B = Bob	97 pounds
C = Caitlin	80 pounds
D = Diane	102 pounds

E = Enrico	? pounds
F = Fran	? pounds
G = Gary	? pounds

   a) Equation: $85 + 97 = 80 + E$

   Solution: $E = $ _____ pounds

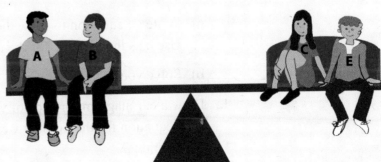

b)

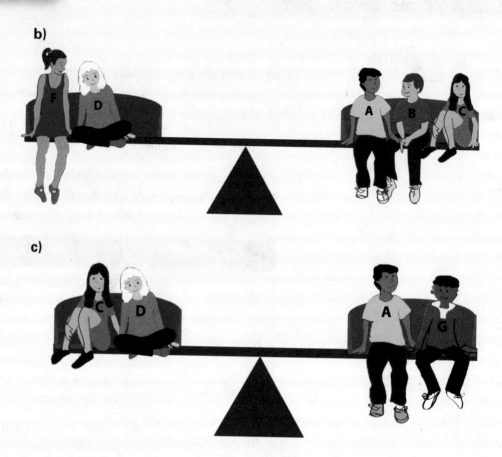

c)

4. Mackenzie filled a bag with peanuts. The clerk put the peanuts on a scale and used weights to balance it as shown below.

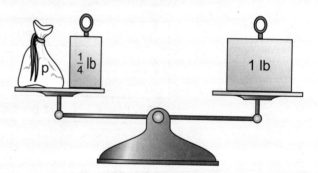

a) Write an equation to show the balance shown on the scale. Use *p* as the variable for the unknown amount of peanuts.

b) Solve your equation for *p*.

5. Draw a bar diagram for each of your equations in Question 3. Solve each equation for the missing weight. Compare your answers to those in Question 3.

6. For each of the following, draw a balance scale or a bar diagram. Write an equation to match your picture. Find the solution to each equation.

   a) Ceila had four ribbons of different lengths:

   Green: 18 inches, Blue: 23 inches, Red: 17 inches, Orange: ? inches

   The total length of the green and blue ribbons is the same as the total length of the red and orange ribbons. How long is the orange ribbon?

   b) Matt drove from his house to his cousin's house. He drove 82 miles and then stopped for gas. He then drove another 20 miles to his cousin's house. On the way back, he drove the same route. After driving for 22 miles, how much farther did he have to drive before getting home?

   c) Ali and Ray each bought the same amount of nuts. Ali bought $2\frac{1}{2}$ pounds of peanuts and 6 pounds of cashews. Ray bought 7 pounds of cashews. The rest of his nuts are peanuts. What is the weight of Ray's peanuts?

7. a) Write a word problem that might be solved using the equation $\$0.45 + n = \$0.82$.

   b) Draw either a bar diagram or a balance scale to illustrate your equation.

   c) Solve the equation for n.

8. Solve each of the following for n. Show your work or explain your thinking.

   a) $825 + n = 258 + 824$

   b) $n + 2\frac{1}{2} = 15 + 3\frac{1}{2}$

   c) $924 + 30 = 900 + n + 4$

   d) $2345 - 398 = n - 400$

   e) $4998 + 3786 = n + 5000$

   f) $8567 + 400 = 60 + 7 + 8000 + n$

Think Beyond

9. In the following diagrams, the numbers in the corners sum to the number in the square between them. For example, in part a,
$A + B = 12$; $A + C = 10$; and $B + C = 4$.
Find the value of each of the variables.

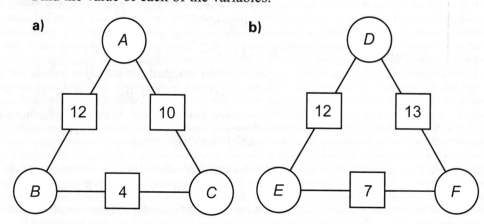

a)

b)

Think Back

10. Compute each of the following. Do not use a calculator and show your work.

a) $37 \cdot 38 =$

b) $21 \cdot 92 =$

c) $245 \div 34 =$

d) $496 \div 45 =$

e) $389 + 182 + 937 =$

f) $4028 - 329 =$

11. Write in simplest form.

a) $\frac{12}{16}$

b) $\frac{88}{12}$

c) $\frac{18}{10}$

d) $\frac{21}{6}$

12. Shamika bought 3 pounds of fish at $3.98 per pound.

a) How much will her bill be?

b) How much change should she get back from a $20 bill?

13. If Corinne paid $15.96 for 4 pounds of fish, how much did the fish cost per pound?

14. True or False? All squares are rectangles. Explain.

Divide and Conquer

LESSON 1.3

Start It Off

Paco's teacher wrote $95 + 87 + 205 = $ _____ on the board. Paco found the answer in just a couple of seconds. Shirlee asked him how he did it. Paco said he first thought $(95 + 87) + 205 = (87 + 95) + 205$.

1. What is the name of the property that told Paco that $95 + 87 = 87 + 95$?

Paco then said that $(87 + 95) + 205 = 87 + (95 + 205)$. The property that states that you can group addends differently without changing the answer is the associative property of addition. There is also an associative property of multiplication.

2. How did using the associative property help Paco to find this sum quickly?

3. Solve the following using the commutative and associative properties of addition and multiplication.

    a) $18 + 427 + 82 = $ _____

    b) $2998 + 487 + 302 = $ _____

    c) $5 \cdot 83 \cdot 2 = $ _____

> **MATHEMATICALLY SPEAKING**
>
> ▶ associative property of addition
> ▶ associative property of multiplication

For over 2000 years, traders have worked at the great bazaar in Kucha, China. This was the crossroads of the Silk Road, an ancient trade route from China and India to Europe and Africa. It is still a major trading post. Because of the Silk Road, both products and ideas were spread around the world. The Persian Mohammed Al-Khwarizmi used the Hindu-Arabic number system to develop algebra over 1000 years ago. This system used numerals originally developed in India and spread through Europe from this work done by Al-Khwarizmi. Today the universal language of mathematics lets people from around the world communicate with each other. Expressions like $18 + 427 + 82$ mean the same thing to everyone.

Let's Trade: Evaluating Expressions and Solving Equations

MATHEMATICALLY SPEAKING

▶ evaluate (an expression)

Algebra is sometimes called the language of mathematics. It has some words and phrases that have very specific mathematical meanings. Some of these words are *equation, variable* and *expression*. When you substitute a number for a variable in an algebraic expression and perform the operations, we say you are evaluating the expression.

Example

The expression $5 + w$ might represent the weight of a catfish that weighs 5 pounds more than a trout that weighs w pounds. If the trout weighs 7 pounds, then you might write:

Weight of trout: w

Weight of catfish: $5 + w$

The trout weighs 7 pounds: $w = 7$

Substitute 7 for *w* and evaluate the expression: $5 + 7 = 12$

The catfish weighs 12 pounds.

1. In the table below, w is the weight of a trout and the expression gives the weight of a catfish. Describe in words how the weight of the catfish is related to the weight of the trout. Find the weight of the catfish if the trout weighs 6 pounds. The first one is done for you.

Expression for the Weight of the Catfish	Meaning of Expression	Weight of the Catfish for $w = 6$ pounds
$w + 8$	The catfish weighs 8 pounds more than the trout.	$6 + 8 = 14$ pounds
$w \div 2$		
$2 \cdot w$		
$w - 2$		

Imagine the following scene on the Silk Road hundreds of years ago. Note that fruits of the same type in the same problem all weigh the same amount.

Hamed is helping his father set up a stall at the Kucha bazaar. He placed mandarin oranges on the following scale.

3 bags and 2 loose oranges   20 loose oranges

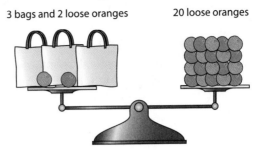

2. Hamed has put the same number of oranges in each bag. The first customer notes that there are 20 loose oranges that balance the three bags and two loose oranges. The customer wants to figure out how many oranges are in each bag. He first takes two oranges off of each side of the scale.

a) After taking two oranges off each side, what is left on each side of the scale?

b) The customer then said that he knew how many oranges were in each bag. He said he used two strategies: remove and divide. Explain what he did.

c) To represent the oranges on the scale, Hamed wrote: $3m + 2 = 20$. Another customer said that $3m + 2$ meant three mandarin oranges plus two more. She said that this was not right because it would mean that 5 were equal to 20. Hamed said that the m stood for the number of oranges in each bag. The 3 meant that there were three bags and the 2 represented the two oranges left over. He said the expression $3m + 2$ described the total number of oranges. Who was right? Explain.

d) Evaluate the $3m + 2$ using the number of mandarin oranges in each bag for m. How is this related to Hamed's equation $3m + 2 = 20$?

3. On another scale four bags and four loose apples balanced 32 loose apples. Each bag contained the same number of apples.

4 bags and
4 loose apples   32 loose apples

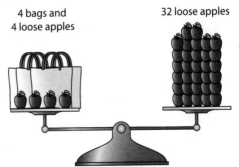

a) Write an equation that Hamed would use to describe this balance puzzle. Use a to stand for the number of apples in each bag.

b) Use the strategies of remove and divide to find the number of apples in each bag. Explain your method. How is this related to your equation in Part a?

4. Hamed set up three scales as shown below. The bags within each balance puzzle contain the same number of objects. Write an equation for each balance puzzle. Explain what your variable stands for and solve your equation. Be prepared to discuss your solution.

a)

45 pears

4 bags of pears; 1 loose pear

b)

82 figs

6 bags of figs; 10 loose figs

c)

95 dates

15 bags of dates 5 loose dates

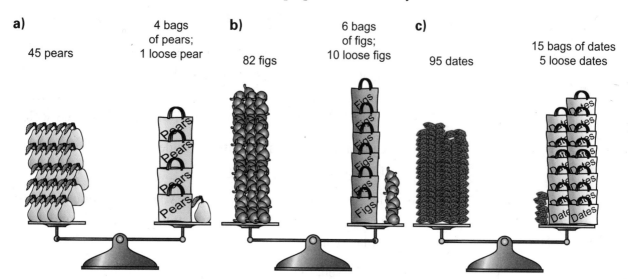

5. Hamed has six bags of bananas with two loose bananas. These bags are not on a scale. Hamed always puts the same number of bananas in each bag.

a) Write an expression for the total number of bananas. How many total bananas might there be? Give at least three different amounts.

 **Hint**
See page 167

b) Explain how you found the answer.

6. a) Create a story problem using the equation $4a + 3 = 23$. Explain the meaning of the numbers 4, 3, 23 and the variable a.

b) Solve the equation for a. What is the meaning of this solution?

c) Is there more than one possible answer for a? How do you know if an equation has a single correct solution? How do you know if an equation has more than one solution?

Trading Tables: When Do Variables Vary?

Hamed's sister Maysoon makes charts to keep records of sales. She knows that Hamed might sell four bags of bananas to two different customers. But she also knows that different bags might contain different numbers of bananas. So, if she writes an algebraic expression with a variable that represents the number of bananas in a bag, that variable can have several different values. For each different value, the value of the entire expression will change.

7. Maysoon has made the following table. It shows the total number of cucumbers sold if she sells three bags and two loose cucumbers. She always puts the same number of cucumbers in each bag.

Number of Cucumbers in Bag, c	Total Number of Cucumbers, $3c + 2$
0	2
1	5
2	8
3	
4	

a) Copy and complete the table to show the total number of cucumbers sold. List two patterns that you see on the table.

b) What does the c in the expression $3c + 2$ stand for?

c) What is the meaning of the 3 and the 2 in the expression $3c + 2$?

d) If there are 12 cucumbers in a bag, how many total cucumbers are there? Write an equation to show your solution.

e) If there are 26 total cucumbers, how many are there in each bag? Write an equation that describes this situation. Solve it to find the number of cucumbers in each bag.

8. Maysoon has four bags of potatoes with two loose potatoes left over. There are p potatoes in each bag.

    a) Write an expression for the total number of potatoes.

    b) What is the meaning of each number and variable in your expression?

    c) Copy and complete the table using your expression.

Number of Potatoes in Bag, p	Total Number of Potatoes
3	14
2	10
6	
4	
20	
12	
15	

    d) Compare this table to the one that Maysoon used for the cucumbers. Which table was harder to finish? Why? What should Maysoon do when designing these tables?

Wrap It Up

- What is the difference between an expression and an equation? Give an example of each.

- What does it mean to evaluate an expression?

- How many values are there for the variable in $3m + 7$?

- Make a story problem that might be represented by $3m + 7$. Be sure to explain the meaning of the numbers 3 and 7 as well as the variable m.

- For your situation, what does $3m + 7 = 34$ mean?

- Explain how you would solve the equation $3m + 7 = 34$ for m. What is the meaning of the solution in your story? How many values of m solve this equation?

- With a partner, compare situations where there is more than one possible value for a variable to situations where only one value is possible.

MATHEMATICALLY SPEAKING

- ▶ associative property of addition
- ▶ associative property of multiplication
- ▶ evaluate (an expression)

On Your Own

 **Write About It**

1. Hamed put 46 figs into bags, with the same number of figs in each bag. He wrote the equation $8f + 6 = 46$ to indicate how many bags and loose figs he had.

   a) Explain the meaning of 8, 6, 46 and the variable f in this equation.

   b) Describe how you would use the remove and divide strategies to find the number of figs in each bag.

   c) Is there more than one value for the variable that makes this equation true? Why or why not?

2. Jenna wrote the expression $j + 5$ to stand for her age 5 years from now.

   a) If Jenna is currently 15 years old, evaluate the expression $j + 5$.

   b) If $j = 13$, evaluate the expression $j + 5$.

   c) How many different values for j might be used in this expression?

3. Write an expression to represent each of the following:

   a) The total cost of movie tickets for p people if each ticket costs $6.75.

   b) The amount of money you would earn in h hours if you make $4.50 per hour.

   c) The area of a rectangle with a length of 5 cm and a width of w cm.

4. Evaluate each of your expressions in Question 3a–c:

   a) If the value of the variable in each expression is 3.

   b) If the value of the variable in each expression is 12.

5. Match each expression in the first column with the phrase in the second column.

$a + 6$	The cost of 6 apples if 1 apple costs a dollars.
$6a$	Andy's age 6 years ago if his current age is a.
$a - 6$	Andy's age in 6 years if his current age is a.
$a \div 6$	The cost of 1 apple if 6 apples cost a dollars.

6. Evaluate each of the following expressions when the value of the variable n is 12.

   a) $6n + 8$

   b) $6 + n + 8$

   c) $n \div 6 + 8$

   d) $n - 6 + 8$

7. a) Copy and complete the table for Maysoon, who has six full bags of carrots plus three loose carrots.

Number of Carrots in Bag, c	Total Number of Carrots
0	3
1	9
2	
3	
4	
5	

   b) How many possible values are there for c in Maysoon's chart?

   c) List two patterns that you notice on the chart.

   d) Maysoon has 57 total carrots. If she still has six bags and three carrots left over, write the equation.

   e) Use the remove and divide strategies to solve your equation.

   f) How many possible solutions are there for your equation? Explain.

8. Li Chin sells boxes of beads at the market. Julio bought three of the same size boxes and two loose beads. When he counted them, he found that he had 38 beads.

   a) Write an equation for this situation. Use b for the number of beads in each box.

   b) Solve your equation for b. What is the meaning of your answer?

9. At the market, Sabrina bought three bags of peanuts for her elephant. The peanut seller gave her five extra peanuts. When Sabrina counted them, she found that each bag had the same number of peanuts.

   a) Write an expression that represents the total number of peanuts. Use p for the number of peanuts in each bag.

b) Copy and complete the table for this situation.

Number in Bag, p	Total Number of Peanuts
0	5
1	8
2	11
3	
4	
5	
6	
7	

c) How many values for p are there on Sabrina's chart?

d) If Sabrina had 65 peanuts, write an equation for this situation.

e) Solve your equation for p. How many peanuts were in each bag? Is there more than one value for p that will solve this equation?

f) If there were 62 peanuts in each bag, how many total peanuts would Sabrina have?

10. Charley had $37. He bought five T-shirts. Each T-shirt cost the same amount. He had $2 left over.

a) Charley wrote $5t + 2 = 37$. What is the meaning of 5, 2, 37 and the variable t in this equation?

b) Solve the equation for t. What does the t represent? Is there more than one possible value for t that will solve this equation?

11. Tyler saves his nickels at the end of each day. One day, he decided to put all his nickels in rolls to take to the bank. He put the same number of nickels in each roll. After he did this, Tyler had three full rolls and 12 nickels left over.

a) Write an expression for the total number of nickels Tyler had. Use n as the variable for the number of nickels in each roll.

b) Write an equation that represents this situation if Tyler has a total of 132 nickels.

c) Solve your equation for n. How many nickels are there in each roll?

d) Tyler deposited all his full rolls in his account. How much money did he deposit?

12. Ms. Graves rides the bus to school and back home every day. The bus fare is $1.35 each way.

  a) How much does Ms. Graves spend on bus fare each day?

  b) Write an expression to show the amount of money that Ms. Graves spends on bus fare in d days.

  c) Write an equation if Ms. Graves spent $35.10 on bus fare.

  d) How many days did it take Ms. Graves to spend $35.10?

13. Ms. Graves's house is 12 miles from school.

  a) How many miles does Ms. Graves travel to school and back each day?

  b) Ms. Graves has traveled a total of 192 miles to school and back. Write an equation using d as the number of travel days with 192 miles of total travel.

  c) Solve your equation for d. Explain the meaning of your solution.

Think Beyond

14. Jean wrote the equation $5c = \$44.95$ to describe how much she spent buying boxes of candy. Sue said that Jean must have bought five boxes of candy that cost c dollars each. Fariba said she bought c boxes of candy that cost $5 each. Who do you think was right? Explain.

Think Beyond

15. Greg packs the same number of apples every Saturday for a picnic. He always packs equal numbers of apples in each bag. He has 1 apple left over when he puts two in each bag, two apples left over when he puts three in each bag, three apples left over when he puts four in each bag and no apples left over when he puts five in each bag. Greg packs fewer than 50 apples. How many total apples does he pack for each picnic? Explain your reasoning.

16. Put the following in order from the least to the greatest:

    a) 0.12   0.112   0.1   0.0115

    b) $\frac{4}{5}$ $\frac{4}{6}$ $\frac{4}{9}$

    c) $\frac{4}{3}$ $\frac{8}{3}$ $\frac{5}{3}$

17. Identify the place value of the 4 in each of the following numbers:

    a) 23,456.21

    b) 423,231,367.351

    c) 35,908,980.24

18. Jean said that to divide 545 by 5, you could first divide 500 by 5 and then divide 45 by 5 and add the two numbers together. Was she right? Explain.

19. Solve for n. $300 + n = 298 + 406$

20. Write a story problem that fits the equation in Question 19. What is the meaning of the variable in your problem?

Combine, Simplify and Solve

➡️ Start It Off

A multiplication-and-division fact family is a set of related facts. Once you learn one fact, you can use the commutative property of multiplication and the relationship between multiplication and division to figure out the others. For example, if you know that $4 \cdot 8 = 32$, you also know that $8 \cdot 4 = 32$, $32 \div 8 = 4$ and $32 \div 4 = 8$. The fact family for the numbers 2, 3 and 6 is $2 \cdot 3 = 6$, $3 \cdot 2 = 6$, $6 \div 2 = 3$ and $6 \div 3 = 2$. The fact family for the numbers 2, 2 and 4 is $2 \cdot 2 = 4$ and $4 \div 2 = 2$. Why are there only two equations in this family?

For each of the following, list as many fact families as you can. Each fact family uses three different numbers or the same number twice with a third, different number.

1. 42, 6, 7

2. 8, 56, 7, 4, 2, 28

3. 4, 8, 16, 32, 64

Combining Constants and Like Terms

As you have seen in this section, you can write expressions to describe situations or represent amounts or values. You have written expressions to find the weights of coins and fruits and the costs of different items. When two expressions are equal, you can show that by writing an equation.

1. Meredith had six boxes with p pencils in each box and four loose pencils. Tony had two boxes of pencils with the p pencils in each box and three loose pencils.

   a) Write an expression for the number of pencils Meredith has. Write another expression for the number of pencils Tony has.

   b) Write an expression for the total number of pencils Meredith and Tony have.

   c) Discuss with a partner how you combined the expressions.

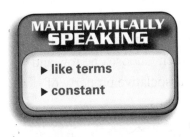

MATHEMATICALLY SPEAKING
- like terms
- constant

Once you write a combined expression, you can simplify it by combining like terms. Like terms are terms that contain the same variable. For example, $6p$ and $2p$ are like terms because they both contain the variable p. You can combine $6p$ and $2p$ to get $8p$ just as you may have combined the 6 boxes of pencils and 2 boxes of pencils to get 8 boxes of pencils. You can also combine all the constants. Constants are numbers that do not change, such as 4 and 3. If you had 3 loose pencils and 4 more loose pencils, these combine to give you 7 loose pencils.

2. Justine and Megan were discussing the expression $5a + 3$. Justine said that this is the same as $8a$ and Megan disagreed. Megan said this expression could represent five bags of apples with the same number of apples in each bag and three loose apples. She says this would not be the same as eight bags of apples with the same number of apples in each bag. Discuss with a partner whether Justine or Megan is correct.

3. On Monday, Mr. Gibson bought five notebooks for n dollars each and three pens for p dollars each. He wrote the expression as $5n + 3p$ to show the total cost of his purchases. On Tuesday, he bought two more notebooks and five more pens.

   a) Write an expression for the cost of his purchases on Tuesday.

   b) How many notebooks and how many pens did Mr. Gibson buy all together? What do you think it means to combine like terms?

   c) Write an expression for the total cost of the notebooks and pens that Mr. Gibson bought.

   d) Compare your answers with a partner's. Be prepared to discuss this with your class.

4. Kelly bought five CDs at c dollars each and four T–shirts at t dollars each. LaShawn bought two CDs at c dollars each and seven T–shirts at t dollars each.

   a) Write an expression to show the cost of Kelly's purchases. Write an expression to show the cost of LaShawn's purchases.

   b) Write an expression to show the total cost of Kelly's and LaShawn's combined purchases. Combine like terms in your expression.

   c) Discuss with a partner how you combined expressions and like terms. What is the meaning of the c and the t in your expressions?

5. Copy and complete the table by adding the expressions in Column A and B. Combine like terms and constants and write the resulting expression in Column C. Compare your results with a partner. Choose one row and explain how you used the commutative and/or associative property of addition to combine the first and second expressions.

A. First Expression	B. Second Expression	C. Sum of Expressions in A and B
4a + 7	8 + 6a	
2t + 3s + 7	5 + 4s	
18 + 7x	3y + 9	
15	4a + 8	
15a + 4b + 2	6b + 8 + 2a	

Equivalent Expressions

MATHEMATICALLY
SPEAKING

▶ equivalent expressions
▶ equivalent

Two expressions that always have the same value are called equivalent expressions. When you have two equivalent expressions with an equal sign between them, you have an equation. You have used equations throughout this section to show that an expression was equivalent to or balanced with, another expression or a number.

6. a) For each equation, tell whether the statement is always, sometimes or never true for any whole number. For each, give an example using whole numbers for the variables. If the statement is sometimes true, give one example where it is true and one where it is false.

Hint
See page 167

Equation	Always, Sometimes, Never True	Example(s)
$n - 0 = n$	always true	$3 - 0 = 3$
$5 \cdot a = a \cdot 5$		
$2 - b = b - 2$		
$(3 \cdot 2) \cdot c = 3 \cdot (2 \cdot c)$		
$d \cdot 1 = 1 \cdot d$		
$n \div 1 = 1 \div n$		
$5t + 2t = 7t$		
$3n + 4 = 7n$		

b) Which equations above are always true? Do you notice a pattern?

c) In which equations is there only one solution? Which have an infinite number of solutions? Which have no solutions? Do you notice a pattern?

7. a) For the following rectangle, Brent said you could find the perimeter by adding $3 + 5 + 3 + 5$. Jody said you could find the perimeter by evaluating $2 \cdot 3 + 2 \cdot 5$. Who is right? Explain.

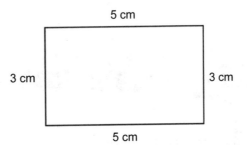

b) For the following rectangle, Jared said you could find the perimeter by adding $w + l + w + l$. Jody said that you could find the perimeter by evaluating $2 \cdot w + 2 \cdot l$. Who is right?

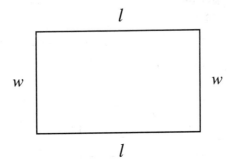

c) If the length of the rectangle is 15 feet and the width is 6 feet, evaluate both expressions: $w + l + w + l$ and $2 \cdot w + 2 \cdot l$. What is the perimeter of the rectangle using each expression?

d) Does $w + l + w + l = 2 \cdot w + 2 \cdot l$ for any values of l or w? In other words, are $w + l + w + l$ and $2 \cdot w + 2 \cdot l$ equivalent expressions? Explain. Include the use of the associative and/or commutative properties in your explanation.

8. a) Caleb said that $5n + 2 = 7n$. Choose a whole number value for n and evaluate the expression $5n + 2$ and the expression $7n$. Are the two expressions always equivalent? Is Caleb's equation ever true? Explain.

b) Parker said that $2a + 7 + 3a = 12a$. Kayla said that $2a + 7 + 3a = 5a + 7$. Choose a value for a and evaluate the expressions in both equations. Was Parker or Kayla correct? Could both be correct? Explain.

Wrap It Up

• What does it mean to combine two expressions? What does it mean to combine like terms in an expression?

• How do you use the associative and/or commutative properties of addition or multiplication to combine like terms?

• How do you determine whether two expressions are always equal, sometimes equal or never equal? When are two expressions equivalent?

• How can you use evaluation of expressions to help determine whether two expressions are equal?

 **Write About It**

1. **a)** Describe a situation that can be represented by the expressions $3n + 8$ and $2n + 6$.

   b) Combine the two expressions and describe what the result means in your situation.

2. Evaluate each of the following expressions for $n = 5$ and $a = 2$.

   a) $7n + 2$

   b) $6a + 3 - n$

   c) $a + 14a + 2n + 7$

3. **a)** For each of the following equations, tell whether the statement is always, sometimes or never true for all whole numbers. For each, give an example using whole numbers for each of the variables. If the statement is sometimes true, give one example where it is true and one where it is false.

Equation	Always, Sometimes, Never True	Example(s)
$a + b = b + a$		
$3 \cdot (6 \cdot c) = (3 \cdot 6) \cdot c$		
$c \cdot 96 = 96 \cdot c$		
$32 + (45 + d) = 32 + (d + 45)$		
$5t + 6 = 11t$		
$2a + 3b + 6a + 4b = 8a + 7b$		

   b) Which of the equations are always true? How can you tell?

4. Darius said that $7n + 5 = 12n$ for all values of n. Was Darius right? Explain.

**Think
Beyond**

5. For each of the following, choose a different one–digit number for each box that will give you the largest answer for each expression. For example, in Part a, determine whether you should have 98 • 7, 87 • 9, 97 • 8 or some other choice to give you the largest product. Justify your choices.

a) ☐☐ × ☐

c) ☐☐ – ☐☐

b) ☐☐ ÷ ☐

d) $\frac{☐}{☐} + \frac{☐}{☐}$

**Think
Back**

6. Write each number in words.

a) 239,728   **b)** 47,098.114   **c)** 708,009.03

7. Five rubies at the Egyptian market cost $259.45 each and a diamond costs $678.92. What is the total price for the six jewels? Show your work.

8. How many 89¢ grapefruit can Mr. Jackson buy at the market with a $5 bill? How much change will Mr. Jackson get? Show your work.

9. Thomas wanted to know how much change he should get from a $20 bill after paying $12.82 for dinner. He said that he could subtract $12.00 from $20.00 to get $8.00 and then subtract $0.82 from that. Kia said that he should first subtract the $0.82 and then subtract $12.00. Kris said he should subtract $12.00 and then add $0.82. Who was right? Explain.

10. Write an expression for each of the following ages. Explain what your variable and the expression means. Evaluate your expression if Mr. Jackson's age is 52.

a) Mr. Jackson's son is half his age.

b) Mr. Jackson's daughter is 25 years younger than he is.

c) Mr. Jackson's wife is 2 years older than he is.

**Optional Technology Lesson
for this section available
in your eBook**

Sum It Up

In this section you explored how to make sense of numbers, symbols and the concept of equality. You found that it was important to look for patterns with numbers and operations as well as in the world around you.

Balance and Equality

Balance scales and bar diagrams show the balance between two sides of an equation. If you know that two four-ounce tomatoes have the same weight as a pear of an unknown weight and a five-ounce banana, you can draw a balance scale like:

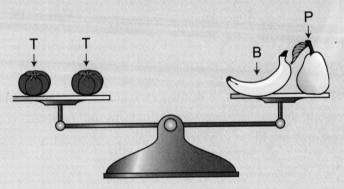

This can be shown with bars as:

T = 4 ounces	T = 4 ounces
P = ? ounces	B = 5 ounces

■ Equations can be used to represent equal amounts. In this example, you might write $4 + 4 = n + 5$. Using balance scales, bar diagrams, balance or equations, the weight of the pear would be 3 ounces.

Variables, Constants, Expressions and Equations

■ Variables can be used to represent unknown quantities in expressions and equations. In the example above, the variable n represents the weight of the pear.

■ Variables may represent quantities that vary or have more than one value or quantities that have only a single value. For example, in the equation, $4 + 4 = n + 5$, only the value $n = 3$ makes the equation true. In the equation, $8 = a + b$, there are many values for a and b that would make the equation true.

■ An expression is a combination of one or more numbers, variables and operations. The following are examples of expressions:

$a + b$ 5 $2n$ $45 - 7c + 10$

■ An equation consists of two expressions that are set equal to each other. The following are examples of equations:

$a + b = 5$ $2n = 34$ $5 - 7c = 45$

■ Equations can be always true ($a + b = b + a$), sometimes true ($a + b = 5$) or never true ($6 + 5 = 10$)

■ Pictures, tables, diagrams, words, symbols, variables, expressions and equations can be used to represent and analyze everyday situations and patterns. For example, the following expressions might be used to represent these situations:

$a + 6$ Andy's age in 6 years if his current age is a

$6a$ The cost of 6 apples if 1 apple costs a dollars

$a - 6$ Andy's age 6 years ago if his current age is a

$a \div 6$ The cost of 1 apple if 6 apples cost a dollars

Simplifying and Evaluating Expressions and Solving Equations

Expressions can be simplified by combining constants and like terms. For example, in the expression $5n + 9 + 3b + 4 + 2n$, the terms $5n$ and $2n$ can be combined as $7n$. The 9 and 4 can be combined as 13. The simplified expression is $7n + 3b + 13$.

An expression can be evaluated by substituting numbers for the variables and performing the operations. To evaluate the expression $7n + 3b + 13$ for the values $n = 2$ and $b = 5$, substitute 2 and 5 in the expression for n and b. The expression is then $(7 \cdot 2) + (3 \cdot 5) + 13$. This is equal to $14 + 15 + 13$ or 42.

An equation can be solved by finding a value for each variable that makes the equation a true statement. For example, if $6 + 8 = n + 2$, you know that n must be equal to 12 to make the two sides of the equation balance: $6 + 8 = 12 + 2$.

Properties of operations such as the commutative property of addition, the commutative property of multiplication, the associative property of addition and the associative property of multiplication can be used to simplify expressions and solve equations.

MATHEMATICALLY SPEAKING

Do you know what these mathematical terms mean?

- associative property of addition
- associative property of multiplication
- bar diagram
- commutative property of multiplication
- constant
- equal
- equation
- equivalent
- equivalent expressions
- evaluate (an expression)
- expression
- like terms
- solution
- solve (an equation)
- variable

Study Guide

Making Sense of Equality

Part 1. What did you learn?

1. In Parts a–c, write an expression to represent each of the following:

    a. The total cost of x CDs if each CD costs $17.

    b. The perimeter of a triangle with sides of length 3, 5, and x units.

    c. The change from a $20 bill after buying a pair of sunglasses for x dollars.

    d. Evaluate each of your expressions for $x = 7$.

    e. Did you write expressions or equations in Part d? How do you know?

2. For each of the following equations, tell whether the statement is always, sometimes or never true. Give a reason or example for each answer.

    a. $n \cdot 0 = 0$

    b. $4m + 1 = 5m$

    c. $13 + x + 7 = 20 + x$

3. In the following balance puzzle, the eggs all weigh the same, the cherries all weigh the same and the grapes all weigh the same. Explain how to use remove and replace to find the number of grapes it would take to balance the egg.

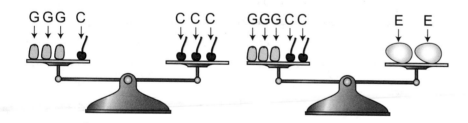
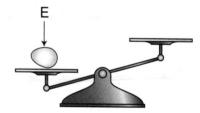

4. Look back at the balance scales from question 3. If each grape weighs 2 ounces, can you determine the weights of the cherry and the egg? Is there more than one possible answer? Why or why not?

5. Sam and Kiara collect baseball and football cards. Sam and Kiara each have the same total number of cards in their collections. Sam has 17 baseball cards and 29 football cards. Kiara has 19 baseball cards. Use a bar diagram to figure out how many football cards Kiara has.

6. Sochea designs and sells beaded bracelets. He puts 12 beads on each bracelet. The expression $12b$ is used to find the number of beads he needs to make any number of bracelets. What does b represent? How do you know?

7. Rafi went to the store on three different days to buy packages of trading cards. There were c cards in each package. Rafi used the expression $18c$ to represent the total number of cards he bought.

   a. Write two expressions to show how many cards Rafi might have bought on each of the three days.

   b. Show that your expressions from part a are equivalent.

8. Joanie solved the equation $n = 302 + 383 + 198$ using properties of addition. Identify each property she used to get from Step 1 to Step 2 and from Step 3 to Step 4. Why do you think she used these properties?

	Step
1.	$n = 302 + 383 + 198$
2.	$n = 302 + 198 + 383$
3.	$n = 300 + 2 + 98 + 100 + 383$
4.	$n = 300 + (2 + 98) + 100 + 383$
5.	$n = 300 + 100 + 100 + 300 + 83$
6.	$n = 883$

9. Marjorie and Rich were solving equations in math class. They looked at one equation in their books and Rich said, "We will need a calculator for this one." Marjorie said, "I can do this in my head if I change the problem to $5 \cdot 20 \cdot 17 = n$? That's an easier but equivalent equation." What might the original equation in the book have been? Which properties is Marjorie using to write this equivalent equation?

10. Fill in the missing information in the chart below.

First Expression	Second Expression	Sum of Expressions in *A* and *B*
a. 15	7*a*	
b. 6*b* + 4		8*b* + 5
c.	10*c* + 8	18*c* + 10

Part 2. What went wrong?

11. Javier tried to use a bar diagram to solve problem 5. Here is what he drew and how he reasoned:

17	29
19	*f*

"Since 19 is 17 + 2, add 2 more to 29 to get 31. Kiara has 31 football cards."

What is wrong with Javier's reasoning?

12. At a local farm stand, cucumbers cost $0.45 each and carrots cost $0.10 each. Lakisha wrote the expression $0.45c + 0.10c$ to represent the cost of buying any number of cucumbers and carrots. Her partner, Diane, said, "We can also write $0.55c$ since 1 carrot and 1 cucumber together cost 55 cents." What do you think about their expressions? Is each an accurate way to represent the cost of buying these vegetables?

13. Kelly was asked the following question on a recent quiz.

> A health food store sells granola by the pound. Andrew bought some granola and paid $6.50 for it. If he bought *p* pounds of granola, which expression could be used to find the cost per pound.
>
> **A.** 6.50*p* **C.** $\frac{6.50}{p}$
>
> **B.** 6.50 + *p* **D.** 6.50 = *p*

Kelly chose letter A because she thought that 6.50*p* meant "$6.50 for one pound."What is wrong with Kelly's reasoning? Which is the correct answer choice? Why?

Using Models and Symbols to Represent Situations

Mathematicians around the world want to be able to communicate easily with each other. Many of the symbols, terms and rules they use are universal and have developed over thousands of years. In this section, you will learn more about some of these symbols, terms, properties and rules. You should have a special place in your mathematician's journal to write these down as you learn them so that you will have a handy reference.

 ## Magical Expressions

Impress your friends by your ability to multiply mentally. Think about the commutative and associative properties and find a shortcut to evaluate the following expressions without using paper and pencil or a calculator. Be prepared to explain your method. The first problem should give you a hint.

1. $(2 \cdot 48) \cdot 5 = (2 \cdot 5) \cdot 48$
$$= 10 \cdot 48$$
$$= ?$$

2. $4 \cdot 9 \cdot 25 =$

3. $20 \cdot 17 \cdot 5 =$

4. $2 \cdot 74 \cdot 5 =$

5. $50 \cdot 42 \cdot 2 =$

Is It Really Magic?

The ancient Pythagoreans were very secretive. Only followers of Pythagoras were allowed to learn the "secrets" of mathematics. The same is often true of magicians today. They do not want people to know their tricks because they want everyone to be astonished by their "magic." In this lesson, you will discover that mathematics is not magic at all or even a trick. You are going to learn how mathematicians use algebraic techniques and strategies.

Mack has a great "magic trick." He knows what answer you will get to this problem before even telling you the clues. Here is his "trick":

Step 1: Think of a secret number.

Step 2: Add 2 to the number.

Step 3: Double your answer.

Step 4: Subtract twice your original number.

Step 5: Write down your final answer.

1. **a)** Try Mack's trick a few times, starting with different secret numbers. Talk to a partner about how you think Mack could always guess the final answer.

   b) Mack drew pictures for each step. The first few steps are done for you. Copy the chart and complete the picture for Step 4. Write the number you get in Step 5.

Directions	Picture
Step 1: Think of a secret number.	n
Step 2: Add 2 to the number.	n $+1$ $+1$
Step 3: Double your answer.	n $+1$ $+1$ n $+1$ $+1$
Step 4: Subtract twice your original number.	
Step 5: Write down your final answer.	

2. Try another one. See if you can figure out the following "magic trick."

> **Step 1:** Choose a two-digit number.
>
> **Step 2:** Double your number.
>
> **Step 3:** Add 7.
>
> **Step 4:** Subtract two times your original number.
>
> **Step 5:** Subtract 5.
>
> **Step 6:** Record your final answer.

a) What is your final answer?

b) Copy and complete the chart below to show how you got the final answer.

Directions	Picture
Step 1: Choose a two-digit number.	n
Step 2: Double your number.	n n
Step 3: Add 7.	n n $+1$ $+1$ $+1$ $+1$ $+1$ $+1$ $+1$
Step 4: Subtract two times your original number.	
Step 5: Subtract 5.	
Step 6: Write down your final answer.	

c) Talk to a partner. Is your final answer the same as your partner's? Is it the same for everyone? How did you figure this out?

3. Here is another "magic trick."

Step 1: Choose a two-digit number.

Step 2: Triple the number.

Step 3: Add 12.

Step 4: Double the result.

Step 5: Divide by 6.

Step 6: Subtract your original number.

Step 7: Record your final answer.

a) What is the final answer?

b) Be prepared to explain the solution method. You may draw pictures or show expressions and equations.

4. Ben wrote a "magic trick" where the final number was the same as the first number, but he got the steps mixed up.

- Double the number.

- Pick a two-digit number.

- Write down your final answer.

- Subtract 10.

- Add 5.

- Subtract your original number.

a) Help Ben put the steps in order.

b) Confirm that your order is correct by trying a couple of different two-digit numbers.

c) Compare your order with your partner's. Do you both have the same order? If not, is there more than one possible correct order?

 Think Beyond

5. David wrote a "trick" where the first three steps were "Pick a secret number," "Add two," and "Triple the result." David would like to have 10 as the answer to his "trick."

a) Write two more steps so that the final answer is 10.

b) Compare your steps with your partner's. Do you both have the same steps? If not, do both methods work?

Think Beyond

6. Sheree wrote a "trick" where the final answer was the number that she started with. Her first three steps were "Pick a secret number," "Add five," and "Double the result."

   a) Write two more steps so that the final answer is the number that she started with.

   b) Compare your steps with your partner's. Do you both have the same steps? If not, do both methods work?

Flowcharts and Backtracking

 **MATHEMATICALLY SPEAKING**

▶ flowchart

LaKeesha said she also could perform mathematical "magic." She said that she could tell you your starting number by knowing only the number that you have at the end. For her "magic," LaKeesha used a flowchart. A flowchart starts with an input, includes some operations and ends with an output. You must follow the direction of the arrows on a flowchart.

Here are the directions LaKeesha's friend Tim followed.

Step 1: Think of a number.

Step 2: Add 2.

Step 3: Multiply by 3.

Step 4: Subtract 5.

Step 5: Tell me your answer.

Tim tried this and said that his answer was 70.

7. To find Tim's beginning number, LaKeesha used the following flowchart.

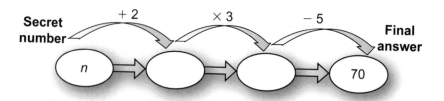

LaKeesha then used what she called "backtracking" to undo the original operations. She started with Tim's final answer and worked backwards as shown in the flowchart below.

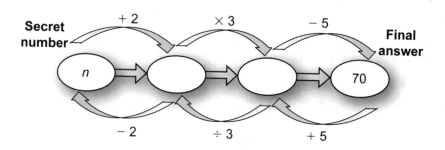

a) Discuss how LaKeesha's backtracking works with a partner. What operation did she use to undo each of the original operations? What was Tim's starting number?

b) Choose a new starting number and tell your partner your final answer. Can your partner use backtracking to find the original number?

8. LaKeesha's second problem was:

Step 1: Choose a secret two-digit number.

Step 2: Multiply by 2.

Step 3: Add 7.

Step 4: Subtract 26.

Step 5: Write down your final answer.

In LaKeesha's backtracking method, she uses opposite operations at each step to go from the final answer back to the original number. These opposite operations are called inverse operations. Addition and subtraction are inverse operations. Multiplication and division are also inverse operations.

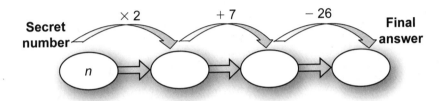

a) Copy the flowchart and record the inverse operations LeKeesha should use to backtrack to find the original number.

b) If the final answer is 55, discuss with you partner how to find the original number.

9. Make up your own flowchart puzzle. Try out the steps with a partner. Be prepared to share it with the class and explain the steps you used to backtrack.

 **W**rap It Up

How might you use pictures, flowcharts and inverse operations to solve a "magic number trick"? In your explanation, use one of the "tricks" in this lesson or one of your own as examples.

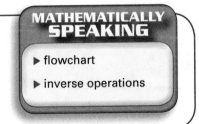

Write About It

1. You are designing a "magic trick," and your favorite number is 5. You want to make sure that everyone gets 5 for the answer. Your steps are:

   Step 1: Pick a number.

   Step 2: Add three.

   Step 3: Double your result.

   Step 4: Subtract 1.

   Step 5:

   Step 6: Record your final number.

   a) Write Step 5 so the final answer in Step 6 is 5.

   b) Use drawings and explain your thinking.

2. Look at the following flowchart.

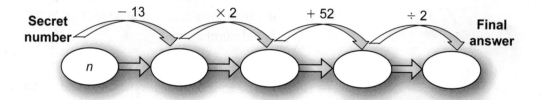

   a) Complete the following steps for this flowchart. The first and last steps are done for you.

   Step 1: Pick a two-digit number greater than 15.

   Step 2:

   Step 3:

   Step 4:

   Step 5:

   Step 6: Record your final number.

   b) If the final answer is 33, what was the original number? Show how you would use backtracking and inverse operations to find the original number.

   c) How would you find the original number given any final number?

3. After you thought of a number, you added 2 and then tripled the sum. At this point, how much larger is your result than triple your original number?

 **Hint**
See page 167

4. Wayne says he has a "magic trick."

   Step 1: Choose a two-digit number.

   Step 2: Add 7.

   Step 3: Double the number.

   Step 4: Subtract the original number.

   Step 5: Subtract 14.

   Step 6: Record your final answer.

   a) Try Wayne's trick. What is the final answer?

   b) Show the steps of the "magic trick" using pictures.

   c) Show the steps of the "magic trick" using a flowchart.

   d) Will everyone get the same answer for this trick? How does the final answer compare to the original number? Explain.

5. Jana also has a "magic trick."

   Step 1: Choose a two-digit number.

   Step 2: Double the number.

   Step 3: Add 5.

   Step 4: Subtract the original number.

   Step 5: Subtract 4.

   Step 6: Record your final answer.

   a) Try Jan's trick. What is your final answer?

   b) Show the steps of the "magic trick" using pictures.

   c) Show the steps of the "magic trick" using a flowchart.

   d) Will everyone get the same answer for this trick? How does the final answer compare to the original number? Explain.

6. Your original number is *n*.

   a) What do you get if you double your number and then add five?

   b) What do you get if you add five and then double your number?

   c) Are your answers for Parts a and b the same? Why or why not?

7. In the following table, some of the directions for the steps are missing.

Directions	Picture
Step 1: Think of a secret number.	*n*
Step 2:	*n* +1 +1 +1
Step 3:	*n* *n* +1 +1 +1 +1
Step 4:	
Step 5: Write down your final answer.	12

   a) What might the directions be for Steps 2, 3 and 4?

   b) What was the secret number? Explain.

8. Some of the steps and some of the numbers are missing in the following flow chart.

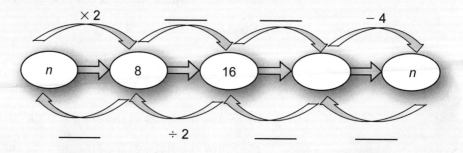

   a) Copy the flow chart and fill in the blanks with the missing steps and numbers so that the diagram makes sense.

   b) Are other steps or numbers possible? Why or why not?

   c) What is the value of *n*? Explain.

9. Think of a number. Add 5. Triple your answer. Subtract 3.

   a) Write two more steps for this magic trick to make the final answer 4.

   b) Explain your thinking in writing the final two steps.

10. Put the following steps in order to create a "magic trick" with a final answer that is twice your original number. Is there more than one way to do this?

    - Write down your final answer.

    - Think of a number.

    - Multiply by 3.

    - Subtract your original number.

    - Add 2.

    - Subtract 6.

11. Write a "magic trick" for an answer that is 1 more than the number you start with. You must have at least 5 steps.

12. Use fractions in one of the tricks in this section. Does it still work? Why or why not?

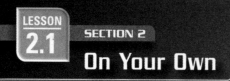

Think Back

13. Myra found that a package of meatballs has 32 meatballs in it. She is having a party with 45 guests and she wants to make sure that she has at least 6 meatballs for each guest. How many packages of meatballs does she need?

14. If each package of meatballs costs $5.45, will $50 be enough to buy the meatballs for the party? (Myra does not have to pay sales tax on food.) If it is enough, how much change will she get back? If not, how much more money does she need?

15. If a package of meatballs weighs two pounds and costs $5.45, about how much would you expect to pay for 6 ounces of meatballs? Explain.

16. Allie said that adding 2 to a number and then tripling it was the same as tripling the number first and then adding 2. Was she correct? Explain.

17. The movie starts at 10:45 am and runs for $2\frac{1}{2}$ hours. What time will the movie end?

   A. 12:15 pm

   B. 1:15 am

   C. 12:45 pm

   D. 1:15 pm

   E. not given

Writing Equations Symbolically

 Start It Off

Mathematicians like to simplify problems. Julie said that she prefers dividing by breaking the dividend apart so that she has two easy problems to solve instead of one hard problem. See if you can figure out what Julie did in the following problems.

$$520 \div 5 = (500 \div 5) + (20 \div 5)$$
$$= 100 + 4$$
$$= 104$$
$$812 \div 4 = (800 \div 4) + (12 \div 4)$$
$$= 200 + 3$$
$$= 203$$

Use Julie's break-up method to solve the following problems:

1. $639 \div 3$

2. $832 \div 8$

3. $575 \div 5$

4. Compare your work with your partner's. Did you break the numbers apart the same way? Did you both get the same answers?

To Market, To Market: Using Mathematical Symbols

Mathematicians like to use symbols as shorthand to represent mathematical relationships and operations. People can easily manipulate symbols rather than the objects they represent. For example, when you were younger, you might have needed to count out 8 pennies and then 5 more pennies by hand to find the total cost of two small pieces of candy that cost 8¢ and 5¢ each. But now, you can simply look at the symbols $8¢ + 5¢ = n$ and know that $n = 13¢$.

About 2,500 years ago, at the end of the Silk Road, there was a flourishing market in Alexandria, Egypt. There were traders, like Isis and her husband Seth, who traded for such things as spices, pottery, precious stones and domesticated animals. Seth made the following chart to show the number of animals that they had for trade.

Animal	Number for Trade
Camels	6
Horses	12
Pigs	20
Ducks	84
Goats	31

Isis used her knowledge of algebra to write equations showing some of the relationships among the numbers of animals. When Isis wrote $2c = h$, she explained to Seth that this meant that if she doubled the number of camels, she would get the number of horses. Note that c stands for the number of camels, so $2c$ means that Isis multiplied the number of camels by 2 to get the number of horses; it does not mean 2 camels.

1. What did Isis mean when she wrote $p - 8 = h$?

2. Seth said that Isis should have written $h + 8 = p$ instead of $p - 8 = h$. How would you respond?

3. What equation might Isis write to show that there are 11 more goats than pigs? Write a different equation that shows the same relationship.

 **Hint**
See page 167

4. Adam, one of the customers, saw the equation $p + 11 = g$ and said that there must be 11 more pigs than goats. Was Adam correct? Why or why not?

5. Write an equation that uses multiplication to show the relationship between the number of horses and the number of ducks.

6. Write an equation that uses division to show the same relationship between the number of horses and the number of ducks.

7. Write three more equations that show some of the relationships among the numbers of animals. Trade your equations with your partner and explain the meaning of each one.

Market Puzzles

Isis and Seth loved to write riddles for their customers. Look at the riddles in the following problems and think like a mathematician as you solve them. That means that you might need to try "guess, test and refine" or you might need to use the techniques learned in the last section with scales and bars such as "remove, replace and divide." Be prepared to explain your thinking.

8. Isis posed the following riddle.

There is a total of nine camels and pigs in the pen. There is one more camel than pig. How many camels and how many pigs are there?

Seth wrote:

c = number of camels, p = number of pigs

$c + p = 9$

$p + 1 = c$

There are _____ camels and _____ pigs.

a) Seth guessed, "There must be five pigs." If Seth is correct, how many camels must there be? Was Seth's first guess correct? How do you know?

b) What should Seth guess next? Why?

c) On Seth's second guess, he tried 4 as the number of pigs and said that there must be 5 camels since the number of camels must be one more than the number of pigs. He then substituted these values into the equation $c + p = 9$. Do these values make the equation true? Substitute the same values for c and p in the equation $p + 1 = c$. Do the values make this equation true as well?

d) Isis said that after Seth wrote his two equations, he could have used the "replace" technique instead of guessing. Isis suggested that he replace the c in the equation $c + p = 9$ with $p + 1$, since c is equal to $p + 1$. The equation then becomes $(p + 1) + p = 9$. Then, Isis said he could remove 1 from both sides of the equation to get $p + p = 8$ and find the value of p that will make this statement true. How many pigs and how many camels are in the pen? How did you determine this?

9. Seth gave Isis the following riddle. If there is a total of 12 horses and ducks in the pen and there are twice as many ducks as horses, how many horses and how many ducks are in the pen? Isis wrote the following two sentences.

$$h + d = 12$$

$$2h = d$$

a) Isis said that she could replace the d in the first equation with $2h$ and get $h + 2h = 12$. Explain her reasoning.

b) Seth said $h + 2h$ is the same as $3h$. Is he correct? Explain.

c) What technique might you use to solve $3h = 12$? How is this similar to the way you solved some of the balance puzzles?

d) How many horses and how many ducks were in the pen?

10. For each of the following riddles, first write two equations that each use two variables. Then think like a mathematician to find the values for each of the variables that make both equations true. Replace the variables with these values to check your answers. For each riddle, be prepared to explain the techniques you used to solve the equations. Think about how the techniques for solving these equations are similar to the techniques you used to solve the balance puzzles.

a) The total number of cows and horses in the pasture is 15. There are three more cows than horses. How many cows and how many horses are there?

b) There are three times as many goats as chickens in the pen. The total number of goats and chickens is 8. How many goats and how many chickens are in the pen?

c) A fruit basket has a total of 27 apples and oranges. There are 13 more apples than oranges. How many apples and how many oranges are in the basket?

d) A ring has a total of 12 diamonds and rubies. There are twice as many rubies as diamonds. How many diamonds and how many rubies are on the ring?

11. For each of the following sets of equations, write a riddle that would match both equations. Solve your riddles for each of the variables.

a) $g + c = 15$

$c - 7 = g$

b) $d - c = 15$

$d + c = 21$

c) $a + b = 11$

$a - b = 5$

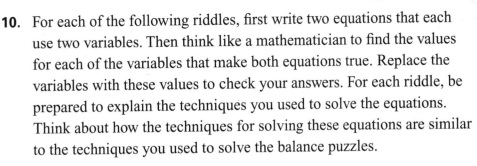 **Think Beyond**

12. Seth has a total of 40 goats, horses and pigs to trade. There are four more pigs than horses. If you add the number of horses to the number of pigs, you will get the number of goats. How many of each kind of animal are for trade? Write and solve equations for this situation. Be sure to explain what your variables stand for.

Think Beyond

13. Write a riddle with your partner about the animals. Do you both agree on a solution? Did you both use the same method to solve the riddle?

Think Beyond

14. There are a total of 54 camels, ducks and goats in the pen. There are eight more goats than camels and one less duck than goats. How many camels, ducks and goats are in the pen? Explain how you figured this out.

⬆ W rap It Up

Mathematicians often use variables as shorthand when writing expressions and equations. How might you use the techniques of replace, remove, divide or guess, test and refine to solve an equation? In your explanation, use the riddles in this section as examples.

LESSON
2.2 SECTION 2

On Your Own

MATERIALS LIST

▶ Lesson Guide 2.5
For On Your Own
Questions 4d and 6

 **Write About It**

1. **a)** Write a riddle that could be represented by the following equations. Explain what the variables stand for.

    $$f + g = 11$$
    $$f = 5 + g$$

    b) Explain how you would use guess, test and refine to solve your equations for f and g.

    c) Explain how you would use replace, remove and divide to solve your equations for f and g.

2. When Isis wrote $3c$, Seth said that meant they had three camels. Was Seth right? Explain.

3. One day, Isis wrote $c = p + 14$ to represent the number of pigs and camels they had. Two customers, Emu and Bisi, disagreed about what this meant. Emu believed that it meant that there were 14 more camels than pigs. Bisi thought that it meant that there were 14 more pigs than camels. Who was right? Explain.

4. For each of the following, write an equation using n as the variable, and then solve for n. Example: "Melody had $9.28 and her dad gave her $12.50 for mowing the lawn. How much money does she have now?" You might write $9.28 + $12.50 = n$, so $n = 21.78.

    a) Ms. Palio drove 23 miles to work, 12 miles to the grocery store, 2 miles to pick up her son at school and then 11 miles to get back home. How many miles did she drive altogether?

    b) Matt bought six notebooks for $0.89 each. How much did he spend altogether?

    c) Sheree spent $25.95 on five T-shirts. If each T-shirt costs the same amount, how much did she spend on each one?

    d) Sal bought a CD for $12.95 and a granola bar for $1.25. How much change did he get back from $20.00?

5. For each of the following equations, write a story problem that it might represent and solve for *n*.

a) $245 - n = 189$

b) $16 = n \div 2$

c) $\$2.98 + \$3.15 = n + \$3.00$

d) $18 \cdot 29 = n$

6. Write riddles for each of the following pairs of equations, tell what your variables stand for and solve each.

a) $p + r = 14$

$r + 4 = p$

b) $s + r = 10$

$4r = s$

c) $8 + m = n$

and

m	$8 + m$
18	

7. Stephen collects stamps. He has a total of 24 stamps from Egypt and China. He has twice as many stamps from Egypt as from China.

a) Write two equations to represent these statements. Use *e* as the variable to represent the number of stamps from Egypt and *c* to represent the number of stamps from China.

b) Find values for each variable that will solve both of your equations. How many stamps does Stephen have from Egypt? How many does he have from China?

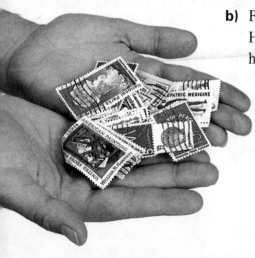

8. Jacob is making a large fruit salad for a school picnic. He is going to use a total of 23 apples and pears. He will use five more apples than pears.

   a) Write two equations to represent these statements. Use a to represent the number of apples and p to represent the number of pears.

   b) Find values for a and p that will solve both of your equations. How many apples and how many pears will Jacob use?

 Think Beyond

9. The pet shop has a total of 28 dogs, cats and rabbits. There are three more dogs than cats. There are two fewer rabbits than cats.

   a) Write three equations to show these statements. Tell what each of your variables stands for.

   b) How many dogs, cats and rabbits are there in the pet shop? Explain your reasoning.

 Think Beyond

10. A rectangle has a perimeter of 24 cm and an area of 32 cm². What is the length and width of the rectangle? Write two equations for this situation. Use l and w as the variables for length and width.

Think Back

11. Solve each of the following equations for *n*. Think like a mathematician and try to solve these without using a calculator, paper or pencil. Explain your reasoning.

   a) $585 + 287 = 288 + n$

   b) $4,908 - 2,987 = 4,900 - n$

   c) $246 \cdot 87 = (246 \cdot 80) + (7 \cdot n)$

12. Find the perimeter of each of the following figures.

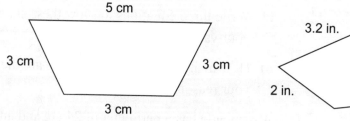

13. Sketch a square with a perimeter of 24 cm. Label the length of each side.

14. Sketch an equilateral triangle with a perimeter of 24 cm. Label the length of each side.

15. Write the symbol <, = or > to make each statement true. Try to do these without a calculator or paper and pencil. Explain your thinking.

   a) $27 + 82$ _____ $82 + 27$

   b) 45×82 _____ $82 + 45$

   c) $90 - 37$ _____ $90 + 37$

   d) $945 \div 1$ _____ 945

   e) $286 \cdot 15$ _____ $(286 \cdot 10) + (286 \cdot 5)$

Out of Order: Using Correct Order of Operations

Start It Off

Jason said that he had another way of breaking division problems apart. He said that sometimes it does not work to just break off the hundreds and divide the two parts. Study the examples of this Jason's method.

Example 1	Example 2	Example 3
$72 \div 6 = (60 \div 6) + (12 \div 6)$ $= 10 + 2$ $= 12$	$120 \div 8 = (80 \div 8) + (40 \div 8)$ $= 10 + 5$ $= 15$	$156 \div 6 = (120 \div 6) + (36 \div 6)$ $= 20 + 6$ $= 26$

Use Jason's method on the problems below. Be prepared to discuss your thinking.

1. $84 \div 7$

2. $96 \div 8$

3. $135 \div 9$

Think Beyond

4. Make up two other division problems of your own and explain how you would use Jason's break-away method to solve them.

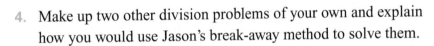

Order of Operations

Look at the following expression:

$$15 - 3 \cdot 4 + 2$$

Alexis says the answer is 50.

Ethan says the answer is 5.

Sam says the answer is 1.

Janice says the answer is 72.

1. Talk to a partner. Can you figure out how Alexis, Ethan, Sam and Janice got their answers? Who do you think is correct?

Hint
See page 167

2. If you have a calculator available, evaluate the expression on your calculator. Compare your answers with classmates who might have a different type of calculator. Did you all get the same result? You might be surprised to find that not all calcuators give the same answers, even though you have typed the same numbers and operations in the same order into the calculator. Scientific calculators will all give the same answer, but some other calculators, especially older models, may give a different result.

Mathematicians had the same problem as Alexis, Ethan, Sam, Janice and some of these calculators. Even for two people from the same country, there was no agreement on what the right answer should be. Therefore, mathematicians from around the world decided that they should all agree on a particular order in which to perform the operations in a mathematical expression. When an expression contained only addition, subtraction, multiplication and division, they decided that they should always do multiplication and division first, from left to right. Then, they would do all the addition and subtraction next, from left to right.

MATHEMATICALLY SPEAKING

▶ convention

This **convention** is a standard that mathematicians have agreed upon so that interpretation is consistent around the world.

3. Now that you know the correct order of operations is "multiply and divide from left to right then add and subtract from left to right," was Alexis right in his thinking when he got an answer of 50? Why not?

4. Talk to a partner and decide whether Ethan, Sam or Janice is correct.

Example

Evaluate $15 - 3 \cdot 4 + 2$.

Step 1: Multiply: $3 \cdot 4 = 12$. Now you have $15 - 12 + 2$.

Step 2: Add and subtract from left to right:
$$(15 - 12) + 2 = 3 + 2 = 5$$

Evaluate $15 \div 3 \cdot 5 + 1$:

Step 1: Multiply and divide from left to right:
$$(15 \div 3) \cdot 5 = 5 \cdot 5 = 25. \text{ Now we have } 25 + 1.$$

Step 2: Add: $25 + 1 = 26$

---

5. Evaluate each of the following expressions. Compare your answers with a partner. Be ready to present justifications for your answers to the class.

a) $38 - 6 \cdot 4 + 2$

c) $15 \cdot 2 + 3 \cdot 6 \div 2$

b) $12 + 24 \div 2 \cdot 3$

d) $48 \div 8 \cdot 2 - 4$

Parentheses

MATHEMATICALLY
SPEAKING

▶ order of operations

The expressions you just looked at involved only addition, subtraction, multiplication and division. But some expressions also include exponents and parentheses. The order of operations takes these things into account. To remember the correct order of operations, some people use the phrase "Please Excuse My Dear Aunt Sally." The first letters of each word stand for: **p**arentheses, **e**xponents, **m**ultiplication, **d**ivision, **a**ddition and **s**ubtraction. That means that you first perform any operations inside the parentheses. You then deal with exponents. And then, as we did above, you perform multiplication and division from left to right and finally, addition and subtraction from left to right.

Example

Let's think about parentheses first. If you have the following expression, $(3 + 2) \cdot (5 - 4)$, you would first add $3 + 2$ to get 5, subtract 4 from 5 to get 1 and then multiply $5 \cdot 1$ to get 5.

6. Evaluate the expression $3 + 2 \cdot 5 - 4$.

a) How does this differ from $(3 + 2) \cdot (5 - 4)$?

b) Why do you get different answers for $3 + 2 \cdot 5 - 4$ and $(3 + 2) \cdot (5 - 4)$?

Sometimes mathematicians use parentheses to avoid confusion, even when the parentheses are not needed For example, if you are evaluating $7 \cdot 3 + 2$, you could write $(7 \cdot 3) + 2$, even though the parentheses are not needed.

7. Evaluate each of the following. Compare your answers with a partner.

a) $(2 + 6) \div 2 \cdot (3 - 3)$

b) $2 + 6 \div 2 \cdot 3 - 3$

c) $2 + 6 \div (2 \cdot 3) - 3$

8. Make up your own expressions to illustrate the correct order of operations and evaluate them. Trade your expressions with a partner. Did you both get the same answers? Check with a calculator. Does the calculator show the correct order of operations?

9. The fraction bar is another way to show division and also acts like parentheses. In the expression $\frac{4+5}{2+1}$, you would first evaluate $4+5$ and $2+1$ to get the fraction $\frac{9}{3}$ and then simplify to get a final answer of 3. Note that another way to write $\frac{4+5}{2+1}$ is $(4+5) \div (2+1)$. Evaluate each of the expressions below. Simplify the fractions if necessary. You might use a calculator that shows fractions in this form to check.

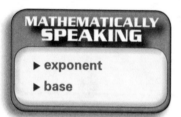

$$\frac{9-1}{3-2} + 12 \cdot 2$$

$$2 \cdot 15 \div 3 + \frac{8 \cdot 3}{4 \cdot 12}$$

$$16 \div 4 \cdot 2 - \frac{3}{2 \cdot 6}$$

Exponents

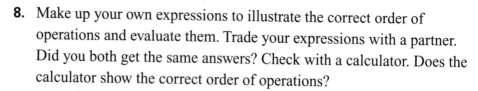

MATHEMATICALLY SPEAKING

▶ exponent
▶ base

Exponents are another type of mathematical shorthand. They are used to show the number of times a factor (the base) is multiplied by itself. For example, the expression 4^3 means that 3 factors of 4 are multiplied. So, $4^3 = 4 \cdot 4 \cdot 4$. In 4^3, 4 is the base and 3 is the exponent. Similarly, 6^4 is shorthand for the product of $6 \cdot 6 \cdot 6 \cdot 6$. In this example, 6 is the base and 4 is the exponent.

10. Use exponents to write $7 \cdot 7 \cdot 7 \cdot 7 \cdot 7$.

11. Write 3^5 using multiplication and evaluate your expression.

12. Write 5^3 using multiplication and evaluate your expression.

13. Emma said that $3 \cdot 5 = 5 \cdot 3$, so $3^5 = 5^3$. Was Emma correct? Explain.

14. Evaluate the following expressions:

   a) 1^5

   b) 0^{12}

   c) $(3-2)^4$

   d) $1^{(12 \times 3)}$

   e) $(3-3)^5$

15. Evaluate the following expressions:

    a) $(3 + 4)^2$

    b) $(4 + 3)^2$

    c) Compare your answers from Parts a and b. Are they the same? Why or why not?

16. Evaluate the following expressions:

    a) $2^3 + 2$

    b) $2^{(3+2)}$

    c) Compare your answers from Parts a and b. Are they the same? Why or why not?

17. Write a^4 using multiplication.

Think Beyond

18. Mathematicians have decided that any number with an exponent of zero is equal to 1. That means that $5^0 = 1$. Which of the following are equal to 1?

    A. 14^0

    B. 0^{14}

    C. $6^{(12-12)}$

    D. $(5 - 5)^5$

Putting It All Together

Now we can look at the entire convention for the order of operations. We know that "Please Excuse My Dear Aunt Sally" reminds us to do the operations in the following order when we evaluate or simplify an expression:

First: Parentheses

Second: Exponents

Third: Multiplication and Division
(Multiply and divide from left to right.)

Fourth: Addition and Subtraction
(Add and subtract from left to right.)

19. Evaluate the following expressions. The first one is done for you.

a) $(2 + 3)^2 - 5 \cdot 2 + 3 = 5^2 - 5 \cdot 2 + 3$

$$= 25 - 5 \cdot 2 + 3$$
$$= 25 - 10 + 3$$
$$= 15 + 3$$
$$= 18$$

b) $2 + 3^2 - 5 \cdot 2 + 3$

c) $2 + 3^2 - 5 \cdot (2 + 3)$

d) $2 + (3^2 - 5) \cdot 2 + 3$

In 1963, Daniel Yovich designed the card game **Krypto** as a fun way to challenge the understanding of the order of operations.

GAME · · · · · · · · · · · Krypto · · · · · · · · · ·

Players: Any number of players or teams of 2

Materials: forty 3 × 5 index cards, four each of the numbers from 1–10 written on the cards (or a regular deck of cards without the face cards)

DIRECTIONS:

- Deal five cards face up so all players can see them.

- Deal a sixth card face up. This is the objective card.

- Each player records as many expressions as possible with a value equal to the objective card, using any or all of the five cards' numbers exactly once and using any combination of operations (addition, subtraction, multiplication, division or exponents).

- Each correct equation scores 1 point. An incorrect equation decreases a player's score by 1 point. If a player can use each of the five cards exactly once using the correct order of operations to get the objective number, that player gets a bonus of 5 points. The player with the highest score at the end of the game wins.

Example: Imagine that the first five numbers placed faceup are $\boxed{5}$, $\boxed{5}$, $\boxed{1}$, $\boxed{2}$, $\boxed{6}$ and the sixth card, the objective card, is $\boxed{8}$. One solution might be $6 + 2$. This would be worth 1 point. A student who says $(5 - 5) \cdot 1 + 2 + 6$ would get 1 point for solving the equation and a bonus of 5 points for using all the numbers. Another bonus possibility might be $6 + 2 \cdot 1 \cdot (5 \div 5) = 8$ or even $1(5 - 5) + 2 + 6$.

 **Think Beyond**

The international tournament rules for **Krypto** specify using a deck of 52 cards: three of each of the numbers 1–10, two of each of numbers 11–17 and one of each number 18–25. Players must always use all five cards with any operations to get the objective card. Try this game with a partner.

Wrap It Up

Explain what is meant by the order of operations. Use several examples in your explanation. Include examples that use addition, subtraction, multiplication, division, exponents and parentheses.

MATHEMATICALLY SPEAKING

▶ base

▶ convention

▶ exponent

▶ order of operations

 **Write About It**

1. **a)** Write three numerical expressions each using at least three of the following:

   - parentheses
   - exponents
   - addition
   - subtraction
   - multiplication
   - division

   b) Evaluate each of your expressions. Choose one of the expressions and explain how you evaluated it using the correct order of operations.

2. Evaluate each of the following expressions using the correct order of operations:

   a) $18 \div 3 \cdot 2 - 4$

   b) $3 \times 2 - 4 \div 2$

   c) $25 - 2 \cdot 3 + 4$

   d) $12 + 3 \cdot 4 \div 2$

3. Evaluate each of the following expressions using the correct order of operations:

   a) $18 \div 3 + 6 \div 2 \cdot 5 - 1$

   b) $18 \div (3 + 6) \div 2 \cdot 5 - 1$

   c) $(18 \div 3) + (6 \div 2) \cdot 5 - 1$

   d) $(18 \div 3) + (6 \div 2) \cdot (5 - 1)$

   e) Are any of the above expressions equivalent? Explain.

4. Add parentheses to make the following equations true:

   a) $4 + 3 \cdot 5 - 4 = 7$

   b) $24 - 12 \div 2 + 4 = 10$

   c) $18 \div 2 \cdot 3 + 5 = 8$

5. Alisha said that $3^4 = 12$. Jared said that $3^4 = 81$. Will said that $3^4 = 64$. Who is correct? Explain.

6. Evaluate each of the following expressions using the correct order of operations. Show your work.

   a) $3 + 3^2 - 4 \div 2$

   b) $(3 + 3)^2 - (4 \div 2)$

   c) $3 + 3^2 - (4 \div 2)$

   d) $3 + (3^2 - 4) \div 2$

   e) Are any of the above expressions equivalent? Explain.

7. Juan evaluated the expression $32 + 3^2 - 14 \cdot 2$ and got 54, which is incorrect. What did he do wrong? What should be the answer?

8. Amber said that $2^4 = 4^2 = 16$. Alexis said that could not be right since 2^3 did not equal 3^2. Who was right? Explain.

9. In the 24 Game®, you get four numbers and use each of them exactly once with any operation to get an answer of 24. For each of the following sets of numbers, use each number only once to get an answer of 24. Be sure to use the correct order of operations.

   a) 5, 6, 6, 1

   b) 3, 3, 4, 1

   c) 5, 4, 2, 8

10. In a game of **Krypto**, the following 5 cards are dealt: 2, 4, 5, 2 and 6. The objective card is 1.

   a) Write an expression equal to 1, using at least 3 of the 5 cards exactly once with any combination of parentheses, addition, subtraction, multiplication and division.

   b) Write an expression equal to 1, using all 5 cards exactly once and any combination of parentheses, addition, subtraction, multiplication and division.

   c) Write an expression equal to 1 using each of the 5 cards exactly once, using at least one exponent and any combination of parentheses, addition, subtraction, multiplication and division.

Think Beyond

Think Beyond

11. Hypatia was an Egyptian female mathematician born in 370 A.D. One of the problems she posed was the following: Find a whole number n, which is the sum of two squares, a^2 and b^2 and whose square is the sum of two other squares, c^2 and d^2.

   a) Write two equations for Hypatia's problem.

   b) Solve your equations for n. Explain your solution.

   c) Can you find another solution?

   ? Hint
   See page 167

Think Back

12. List all the multiples of 7 between 30 and 50.

13. List all the factors of 36.

14. List all the prime numbers between 20 and 40.

15. In the school fund-raiser, for every 5 boxes of cookies that Jen sells, her class gets to keep $2.50. How many boxes of cookies must Jen sell for her class to get to keep $20.00?

16. Find n to make each of the following equations true by giving equivalent fractions.

   a) $\frac{2}{3} = \frac{8}{n}$

   b) $\frac{n}{6} = \frac{8}{12}$

   c) $6 = \frac{n}{5}$

Solving Equations

Start It Off

Cho thinks that sometimes it is easier to multiply first before dividing.
See if you can figure out how Cho does this using the following examples.

$$80 \div 5 = 160 \div 10 = 16$$

$$1{,}200 \div 25 = 4{,}800 \div 100 = 48$$

$$350 \div 50 = 700 \div 100 = 7$$

Try Cho's method yourself with the following expressions:

1. $420 \div 5 =$

2. $340 \div 5 =$

3. $2{,}200 \div 25 =$

4. Why does Cho's method work?

Raising the Bar: Using Bar Diagrams to Solve Equations

Recall that Mei Ling, a student from Singapore, uses bar diagrams to solve equations. Her classmates asked her to show them more about this process. Remember that two bars of the same length "balance" like equal weights on a balance scale or the two sides of an equation.

Two pens and a notebook cost a total of $5.00. Each pen cost $1.25. How much did the notebook cost?

Mei Ling drew the following diagram. (Note that the length of the parts that make up each bar may not be drawn to scale.)

Pen $1.25	Pen $1.25	Notebook $n
$5.00		

After drawing the diagram, Mei Ling wrote the equation:
$1.25 + $1.25 + n = $5.00 and said, "The notebook cost $2.50."

1. **a)** How did Mei Ling solve the problem using the bars?

   b) How might you use the technique of "remove" to solve the equation?

2. Abba bought 82 stamps. Kendra bought 49 fewer stamps than Abba. How many stamps did Kendra buy?

   Abba drew the following bar diagram to represent the situation.

Kendra's stamps (k)	49 stamps
Abba's 82 stamps	

   a) Write an equation for the diagram above. Use k to represent the number of stamps that Kendra bought.

   b) Solve your equation for k. How many stamps did Kendra buy?

3. Sal bought a set of four chairs and a table. Each chair cost $79 and he spent a total of $475 before tax. What did the table cost before tax?

   Sal drew the following bar diagram to show this situation.

$79	$79	$79	$79	table cost (t)
$475				

   a) Write an equation for the diagram above. Use t to represent the cost of the table.

   b) Solve your equation for t. How much did the table cost before tax?

Write an equation and use the bar method to solve Questions 4–7. The equation and bar are shown for Question 4.

4. Trey bought a rosebush and an apple tree. The tree cost $12 more than the bush. He spent a total of $26 before tax. What was the cost of each plant before tax?

Cost of rosebush = r	Cost of apple tree = $r + 12$
Equation: $(r) + (r + 12) = 26$	

5. Julie spent a total of $3.10 buying three apples and two pears. Each pear cost $0.30 more than each apple. What was the price of each pear and each apple?

6. Mr. Kohl drove a total of 270 miles on Monday and Tuesday. He drove 50 miles further on Tuesday than he did on Monday. How far did he drive each day?

7. Ada, Bart and Charley won first place in a robotics competition. The prize was $200. Everyone agreed that Ada did twice as much work as Bart or Charley and should receive twice as much money as each of them. What is a fair way for the three friends to split the $200 prize?

8. a) Write a word problem that you might solve with the following bar diagram.

n	45
92	

b) Write an equation that describes your word problem and solve it.

9. Write your own word problem that includes one or more unknown parts.

a) Draw a bar diagram that represents the situation.

b) Write an equation for your diagram and solve it.

c) Trade word problems with a partner and draw a bar diagram to illustrate your partner's word problem. Write an equation for the bar diagram and solve it.

d) Compare your bar diagram and equation with your partner's. Are your bar diagrams, variables and equations all the same? Did you get the same solution?

 **Think Beyond**

10. a) Write a word problem for the equation $n + 48 = 3n$.

b) Draw a bar diagram that illustrates your word problem.

c) Solve your word problem and explain the solution.

People in different parts of the world at different times in history have solved problems differently. Compare solving an equation using a balance scale to solving an equation using a bar diagram and to solving an equation by using only symbols. Which method do you prefer? Why?

Write About It

1. Garrett said that he could solve riddles using bar diagrams. Explain how you think Garrett might use a bar diagram to solve the following riddle. Solve the riddle using two variables and two equations. Explain the meaning of the variables in the equations. Be sure to include a picture of the bar diagram and the solution in your explanation.

   The pet shop has a total of 18 dogs and cats.

   There are two more dogs than cats.

   How many dogs and how many cats are there in the pet shop?

   Write equations and use the bar method to solve Questions 2–7. Check each answer by using another method of your choice.

2. Jackson has a bulldog and a terrier. The bulldog is 6 inches taller than the terrier. If the sum of the heights of the two dogs is 50 inches, how tall is the terrier?

3. Jackson's bulldog weighs twice as much as the terrier. The two dogs together weigh 144 pounds. How much does the bulldog weigh?

4. Every day Jackson feeds his dogs a total of 12 cups of dog food. The bulldog eats twice as much as the terrier. How much food does the terrier eat each day?

5. Yesterday, Jackson walked his dogs for a total of 55 minutes. He walked the dogs for 13 minutes more in the afternoon than in the morning. How long did Jackson walk the dogs in the morning?

6. When walking the dogs in the park, Jackson counted a total of 92 tulips and daffodils. There were three times as many daffodils as tulips. How many tulips were there?

Think Beyond

7. Jackson saw 26 people in the park. There were twice as many adults in the park as there were girls and there were two more girls than boys. How many boys were in the park?

8. **a)** Write a word problem that you might solve with the following bar diagram.

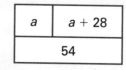

a	$a + 28$
54	

   b) Write an equation that describes your word problem and solve it.

9. **a)** Write a word problem for the equation $b + 48 = 3b$.

b) Draw a bar diagram that illustrates your word problem.

c) Solve your word problem and explain your solution.

Think Beyond

10. Sal bought 3 pounds of peanuts and 4 pounds of cashews. A pound of cashews costs $1.00 more than a pound of peanuts. Altogether, Sal spent $25. How much does a pound of peanuts cost?

a) Draw a bar diagram to show this situation.

b) Explain how you would use the bar diagram to write an equation.

c) How would you find the cost of a pound of peanuts?

Think Beyond

11. There are 20% more girls than boys in the Robotics Club. There are 33 students in the club. How many more girls than boys are there? Explain how you solved the problem.

Think Back

12. Write each of the following as a decimal.

a) $4 + \frac{2}{100} + \frac{5}{10}$

b) $\frac{5}{1,000} + 2 + \frac{7}{10}$

c) $\frac{1}{2} + \frac{9}{100} + 8$

13. There were 400 people at a concert. One-half were men, three-eighths were women and the rest were children.

a) How many of the people at the concert were women?

b) How many more men than children were at the concert?

14. What is the number indicated by the dot on the portion of the number line below?

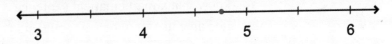

15. Keesha said that $18 + 2 \cdot 3 - 4 \div 2$ was equal to 28. When she checked on her calculator, she got 22. What went wrong?

16. Which of the following numbers are prime and which are composite?

8   15   7   43   1

Looking at Inequalities

Start It Off

In this section, you have seen several ways to divide mentally. Choose one of these methods to simplify each of the following expressions without using paper and a pencil or a calculator. Be prepared to explain your method.

1. $648 \div 6 =$

2. $119 \div 7 =$

3. $828 \div 4 =$

4. $240 \div 5 =$

5. $1,300 \div 50 =$

Understanding Inequality

Robert Recorde was the first person to use the symbol "=", which we know today as an equal sign. He said that he was using two parallel line segments of equal length to represent this idea of equality because no two things could be more equal than parallel lines.

Thomas Harriot, an English mathematician who surveyed land in Virginia in 1585, is said to be the first to use symbols for greater than and less than. Legend said these symbols were based on a symbol he saw on the arm of a Native American while he was in Virginia. He used <, less than, to show that the quantity on the left side was less than the quantity on the right side. He used >, greater than, to indicate that the quantity on the left side of a mathematical statement was greater than the quantity on the right side.

You know that a mathematical sentence is called an equation when an equal sign is used to show that the two sides of the sentence are balanced. The sentence is an inequality when < or > is used to show that the two sides of the sentence do not balance.

When you used the balance scale for weights that were the same on each side, the two sides of the balance were at the same level. On the scale below, you know that the sphere must be heavier than the cube.

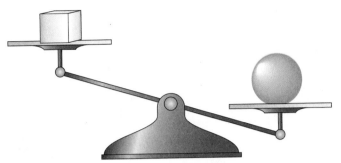

Using s to represent the weight of the sphere and c to represent the weight of the cube, you might write $s > c$ or $c < s$ to show the relationship between the two weights. Another way to show that the two sides of a mathematical statement are not the same is to use the symbol, $\neq$, not equal to. For example, you might write $s \neq c$. This is also an inequality.

1. If the cube on the scale above has a weight of 5 pounds, list four possible weights for the sphere.

2. The scale below is balanced. The cubes weigh the same amount as the sphere.

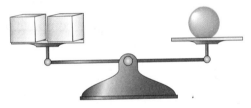

a) Write an equation to show the relationship of the weight of the cubes to the weight of the sphere.

b) If the weight of the sphere is 8 ounces, what is the weight of 10 cubes? Write this weight in pounds.

 Hint
See page 167

c) If the weight of a cube is 500 grams, what is the weight of 6 spheres? Write this weight in kilograms.

 **Hint**
See page 167

3. Use c to represent the weight of the cube and p to represent the weight of the pyramid.

   a) Write two inequalities to show the relationship between the two shapes.

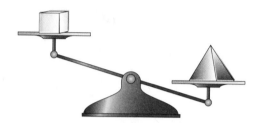

   b) If the cube has a weight of 24 ounces, list three possible weights for the pyramid.

   c) The shapes can be balanced, as shown below. Write one equation for each balanced scale to show the relationships among the weights of the cubes, the spheres and the pyramids.

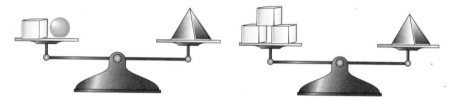

   d) Copy and complete the chart below to show the possible weights of the shapes. In each case, you are given one weight and must find the weights of the other two shapes. The weights in each row must fit the relationships shown on both balanced scales above and the equations from Question 3c.

▲	⬜	⚪
i) 9 pounds	_____ pounds = _____ ounces	_____ pounds = _____ ounces
ii) _____ grams = _____ kilograms	400 grams	_____ grams = _____ kilograms
iii) _____ ounces	_____ ounces	10 ounces

4. **a)** Draw a balance scale to show a cube that weighs more than a pyramid. Write an inequality to show this relationship using c as the weight of the cube and p as the weight of the pyramid.

   b) Write another inequality to show the same relationship.

   c) If the weight of the cube is 4.5 kilograms, list three values for the weight of the pyramid that make your inequality true.

   d) If the weight of the pyramid is $3\frac{7}{8}$ pounds, list three values for the weight of the cube that make your inequality false.

5. For each of the first four equations or inequalities in the table below, state whether it is always true, sometimes true or never true.

   - If it is always true, give one value for the variable that will make it true.

   - If it is sometimes true, give one value for the variable that will make it true and one value that will make it false.

   - If it is never true, rewrite it to make it always true.

   - For the last two, write an equation or inequality that fits the description.

Statement	Always, Sometimes, Never True	Always?—List one value for the variable that makes it true. Sometimes?—List one value for the variable that makes it true and one value that makes it false. Never? —Rewrite the statement to make it true.
$n + 2345 = 6000$		
$2{,}300 + 18 < 19 + 2{,}299$		
$1 \cdot n > 21$		
$1 \cdot n = n$		
		True if $n = 32$; False if $n = 27$
		$n = 7$

Put It Together: Using ≤ and ≥

The inequality symbols ≤ and ≥ each combine two symbols you have already learned about. These symbols are also used in inequalities.

MATHEMATICALLY SPEAKING

▶ symbol "≤"

▶ symbol "≥"

6. Discuss the symbol ≤ with a partner What two previously known symbols are combined to form it? What do you think the symbol means?

7. Carrie said that she does not weigh any more than Jane.

a) What are some possible weights for Jane and Carrie? Could they have the same weight? Could Jane weigh less than Carrie? Could Jane weigh more than Carrie?

b) Carrie wrote $J \geq C$. Do you think that this inequality represents the same thing as the statement above? Explain.

c) Do $C \leq J$ and $J \geq C$ mean the same thing? Explain.

8. Beth is working on her family tree and has made the following chart to show the ages of some of her family members.

Name	Age
Beth	28
Tyron	6
Jake	30
Myra	6
Lisa	52
Gerald	55

a) Beth wrote $T \leq M$. What did she mean? Is it true?

b) Gerald said that she should have written $T = M$. Lisa said she should have written $T \geq M$. Who do you think is correct? Explain.

9. Aiden said that he is at least twice as old as Brandi. He wrote $A \geq 2B$. Brandi thinks that he should have written $2A \geq B$. Who do you think is correct? Explain.

Hint
See page 167

10. If $a \leq b$ and $b \leq a$, how are a and b related? Explain.

11. If $a > b$ and $b > c$, how are a and c related? Explain.

12. Write a situation in words that could be represented by each of the following inequalities:

a) $3 \geq n - 4$

b) $n - 4 \geq 3$

c) Trade your answers with a partner. Do you agree with the situation that matches each inequality?

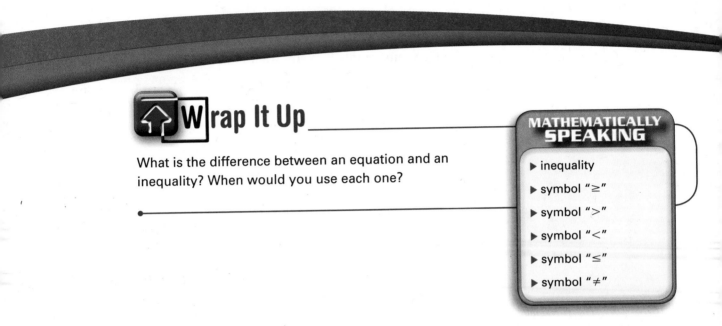

Wrap It Up

What is the difference between an equation and an inequality? When would you use each one?

MATHEMATICALLY SPEAKING

▶ inequality

▶ symbol "$\geq$"

▶ symbol "$>$"

▶ symbol "$<$"

▶ symbol "$\leq$"

▶ symbol "$\neq$"

Write About It

1. It is not always easy for mathematicians to convince other people to use the symbols that they have created as shorthand.

   a) Imagine that you are Thomas Harriot and you are trying to convince your math society to start using the symbol $>$. Write a paragraph with the major points that you want to include in your presentation.

   b) Once you have convinced your society to use the symbol $>$, you decide that they should also use the symbol $\geq$. Write a brief statement to support your argument.

2. Write an inequality or an equation that represents each of the following situations. Include a key for the meaning of each variable.

   a) The number of boys is more than twice the number of girls.

   b) Connor has six more goldfish than Abby.

   c) Jason is less than half of Gena's age.

   d) The number of stamps that Sal has is at least four times the number of stamps that Kara has.

   e) Maxi and Ayla are not the same height.

   f) Two years ago, David was more than twice as old as Julie.

Think Beyond

3. For each of the following inequalities, write a possible situation.

   a) $4n \geq m$

   b) $3 + a < b$

   c) $2c - 5 > d + 2$

4. Use s as the variable that represents the weight of the sphere and c as the variable that represents the weight of the cube.

a) Write two inequalities to show the relationship between the two shapes.

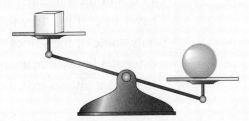

b) If the cube has a weight of 16 ounces, list three possible weights for the sphere.

c) The shapes also balance as shown below. Write one equation for each balanced scale to show the relationships among the weights of the cubes, spheres and pyramids.

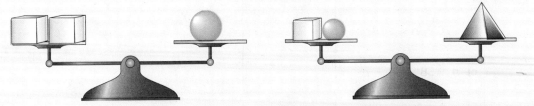

d) Complete the chart below to show the possible weights of the shapes. In each case, you are given the weight of one shape and must find the weights of the other two shapes. Use the relationships from the balanced scales shown and the equations from Part c.

▲	⬜	⬤
i) _____ ounces	_____ ounces	8 ounces
ii) _____ grams = _____ kilograms	600 grams	_____ grams = _____ kilograms
iii) 15 pounds	_____ pounds = _____ ounces	_____ pounds = _____ ounces

5. a) $C \geq D$ and $D \geq C$. Write another equation or inequality that describes the relationship between C and D.

b) $x \geq y$ and $y \geq z$. Write an equation or inequality that describes the relationship between x and z.

6. For each of the statements a–d below, state whether it is true for all values of the variable, true for only some of the values of the variable or never true. If it is true for all values, give one example. If it is true for only some of the values, give one example that will make it true and one example that will make it false. If it is never true, rewrite the statement to make it always true. For items e–f, write a statement that fits the description.

Statement	Always, Sometimes, Never True	Always?—List one value for the variable that makes it true. Sometimes?—List one value for the variable that makes it true and one value that makes it false. Never?—Rewrite the statement to make it true.
a) $n - 282 = 546$		
b) $278 - n < 278$		
c) $n + 58 = 58 + n$		
d) $452 \cdot 12 < 452 \cdot 11$		
e)	Sometimes	True for $n = 4.5$; False for $n = 6.2$
f)	Always	$n = 43$

7. Emma is more than 4 years younger than her brother Adam. She wrote $A > 4 + E$ to show this relationship. Use words and examples to explain whether Emma was correct.

8. Alissa said that if she doubled the amount of money she had, she would still have less money than Taylor.

   a) Write an inequality to show this relationship.

   b) If Taylor has $20, give three amounts of money that Alissa might have.

9. In the computer club, there are more than twice as many girls as boys. There are fewer than 20 members in the club and the girls outnumber the boys by 7.

   a) How many boys and how many girls might be in the club? List all the possible combinations.

   b) What is the greatest total number of students that might be in the computer club? Explain.

Think
Back

10. Use what you know about fractions to fill in the blanks to make the statements true.

   a) $\frac{7}{8} + \underline{\qquad} = 1$

   b) $\underline{\qquad} = \frac{27}{3}$

   c) $1 = \frac{1}{3} \cdot \underline{\qquad}$

11. Which is shorter:

   a) one centimeter or one inch?

   b) one meter or one yard?

   c) one-half of a foot or five-twelfths of a foot?

12. Hartwig wants to display his postcard collection in a scrapbook so that the same number of postcards are on each page. If he has 48 postcards, how many different ways might he do this? List them.

13. Use mental math to find each sum, product or difference.

   a) $98 + 47 = \underline{\qquad}$

   b) $302 - 83 = \underline{\qquad}$

   c) $50 \cdot 16 = \underline{\qquad}$

   d) $2 \cdot 146 \cdot 5 = \underline{\qquad}$

   e) Choose two of the problems above and explain the method you used.

14. Kara said that $\frac{3}{4} + \frac{4}{5} = \frac{7}{9}$. Her calculator gave a different result: $\frac{3}{4} + \frac{4}{5} = \frac{31}{20}$. What did Kara do wrong? What should she do to correct her work?

Optional Technology Lesson for this section available in your eBook

Sum It Up

Flowcharts, Backtracking and Inverse Operations

Mathematical expressions with numbers and variables can be used as a shortcut for describing situations. We can show and evaluate these expressions using a flowchart. For example, you can use a flowchart to find the original number when told the final number to a series of operations such as:

Step 1: Think of a two-digit number.

Step 2: Add 1.

Step 3: Multiply your number by 2.

Step 3: Subtract 5.

Step 4: Tell me your final answer.

If you know that the final answer is 89, you might use the following flowchart to find the original number.

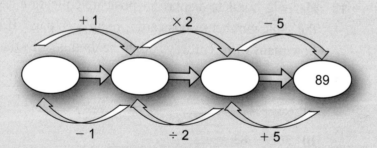

Following the arrows on the bottom, you would first undo subtracting 5 by adding 5 to 89 to get 94. The next step would be to undo multiplying by 2 by dividing 94 by 2 to get 47. You then would undo adding 1 by subtracting 1 from 47. The original number must have been 46. To check this, start with 46, add 1, multiply by 2 and then subtract 5. Is your answer 89?

When one operation undoes another, they are inverse operations. Addition and subtraction are inverse operations. Multiplication and division are also inverse operations.

Writing and Solving Equations Symbolically and With Bar Diagrams

When you solve an equation, you find values for the variables that make the statement true. If you have two equations and two variables, you look for values of the variables that make both equations true. For example, the total number of dogs and cats at the local animal shelter is 45. The number of cats is twice the number of dogs.

■ **Variables:** d = number of dogs, c = number of cats

■ **Equations:** $d + c = 45$ and $c = 2 \cdot d$

■ **Solution:** Replace "c" in the first equation with $2 \cdot d$

$d + (2 \cdot d) = 45$

$3 \cdot d = 45$

$d = 15$

Bar diagrams can be used to illustrate an equation. Two bars of equal length can be used to represent the two sides of an equation. For example, a collar for the dog costs $6.75. I spent $15.00 for dog food and a collar (before tax).

■ **Variables:** f = the price of the dog food.

■ **Equations:** $f + \$6.75 = \$15.00$

■ **Bar diagram:**

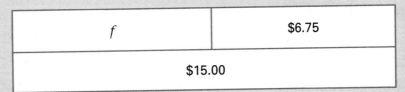

I can find the cost of the dog food by thinking what plus $6.75 equals $15.00. The dog food must have cost $15.00 – $6.75 or $8.25.

Order of Operations

■ Mathematicians have agreed upon a correct order of operations when performing computation.

First: Parentheses

Second: Exponents

Third: Multiplication and Division (Multiply and divide in order from left to right.)

Fourth: Addition and Subtraction (Add and subtract in order from left to right.)

Exponents

Exponents are used as a shortcut to writing the number of times a number is multiplied by itself. For example, 3^4 means $3 \cdot 3 \cdot 3 \cdot 3$.

Note that this is not the same as 4^3. ($4^3 = 4 \cdot 4 \cdot 4$)

Any number with an exponent of 0 is defined as being equal to 1. For example, $4^0 = 1$.

Inequalities

■ The two sides of an inequality are not equal. The symbol $\neq$ can be used to show that the two sides of a mathematical statement are not equal. For example $9 \neq 2 + 8$.

■ The value on one side of an inequality may be greater than ($>$), less than ($<$), greater than or equal to ($\geq$) or less than or equal to ($\leq$) the value on the other side. For example $9 \leq 2 + 8$ and $2 + 8 \geq 9$.

■ There may be many values for a variable that make an inequality true. For example, in the inequality, $2 + n \geq 9$, all values of n that are greater than or equal to 7 will make this statement true.

■ If you know that $a < b$ and also that $b < c$, then you also know that $a < c$.

MATHEMATICALLY SPEAKING

Do you know what these mathematical terms mean?

▶ base

▶ convention

▶ exponent

▶ flowchart

▶ inequality

▶ inverse operations

▶ order of operations

▶ symbol ">"

▶ symbol "$\geq$"

▶ symbol "$<$"

▶ symbol "$\leq$"

▶ symbol "$\neq$"

Study Guide

Using Models and Symbols to Represent Situations

Part 1. What did you learn?

1. Use what you learned in this section about dividing mentally to fill in the table below. There may be more than one possible entry for each cell in the table. Compare your answers with a partner.

Original Problem	Mental Math Strategy	Answer
	$(400 \div 8) + (40 \div 8)$	
$252 \div 4$		
$720 \div 30$		

2. Add two more Steps for the number trick below so that the final answer is your original number.

Step 1	Choose a two-digit number.
Step 2	Add two.
Step 3	Triple your answer.

3. Write a flowchart for your completed number trick from Question 2.

4. Mario drew pictures for each step of a number trick. The square represents the original number and the circle represents a quantity of one. What do you think were the directions for each step? Compare your answers with a partner.

Directions	Picture
	n
	n (+1)
	n n n (+1)(+1)(+1)
	n n n n (+1)(+1)(+1)(+1)
	n (+1)
	(+1)
Step 7: Record your final answer.	(+1)

5. Gus and Sheba solved a number trick. After reading the clues, Sheba said, "My final number is 40." Gus used backtracking to figure out that Sheba's original number was 21. He backtracked by doing $40 + 10$, then $50 \div 2$ and $25 - 4$.

    a. What do you think were the clues of this number trick?

    b. Create a flowchart and record the inverse operations that Gus used to find Sheba's original number on the arrows below the flowchart.

    c. Record the original operations on the arrows above the flowchart.

6. Insert parentheses into each number sentence below to make it true.

    a. $15 - 2 + 3 = 10$

    b. $14 - 2 \cdot 3 = 36$

    c. $4 + 25 - 5 \cdot 4 = 84$

7. Sorboni has only quarters and dimes. She has q quarters and d dimes. She has a total of 15 coins. She has 3 more quarters than dimes.

    a. Write two equations using two variables in each for this situation.

    b. Find the values for each variable that make both equations true. Show your work.

    c. Rewrite the equations with these values replacing the variables to check your answers.

8. Glenda used the following bar diagram to solve a problem about the cost of kneepads and a helmet.

k	$h = 3k$
64	

    a. What might the problem have read?

    b. What is the solution to the problem you wrote?

9. Jim is running a bake sale and is trying to decide how much to charge for brownies and cookies. Jim thinks brownies should cost $1.50 more than cookies. Jim used the following bar diagram to show this.

c	$1.50 + c$
t	

   a. What does each variable and expression represent?

   b. Write an equation for the diagram.

10. Evaluate each of the following:

   a. $(1 + 4)^2 - 2 \cdot 4 + 6$

   b. $1 + (4^2 - 2) \cdot 4 + 6$

   c. $1 + 4^2 - 2 \cdot 4 + 6$

11. Examine the drawings below.

 = 8 kilograms

 = 4000 grams

 = 12 kilograms

   a. Sketch four different scales that show the relationships among the weights of the pyramids, cubes and spheres below.

   b. Write an equation or inequality for each scale you drew.

12. Match each inequality with the correct description. In each description and inequality, n represents the number of nickels and d represents the number of dimes.

   a. The number of nickels that Anna has is more than 3 times the number of dimes she has.

   b. Jim has at least 3 more nickels than dimes.

   c. Nan has at most 3 nickels and dimes.

   d. Mateo has more than 3 nickels and dimes.

   i. $3 + d \le n$

   ii. $d + n \le 3$

   iii. $n > 3d$

   iv. $d + n > 3$

13. State whether each of the following equations is always true, sometimes true or never true.

   - If it is always true, give one value for each variable that will make it true.

   - If it is sometimes true, give one value for each variable that will make it true and one value that will make it false.

   - If it is never true, rewrite it to make it always true.

   a. $4 \cdot n = 24$

   b. $16 - n \cdot 2 = 0$

   c. $p + d = p + d$

   d. $x = x + 3$

Part 2. What went wrong?

14. Bini told his friend that he came up with a quick trick for changing words into an equation. For example, to write an equation for "there are three times as many cucumbers as tomatoes," he did the following:

"there are three times as many cucumbers as tomatoes"

$$3 \quad \times \qquad c \quad = \quad t$$

His friend Marlee said that his equation was backwards and should really be $3 \times t = c$. Who do you agree with? Why?

15. Guy was asked the following question on a recent quiz:

> Ken was playing Krypto. He dealt the following cards: 2, 4, 3, 2 and 3. He created the expression $3 + 3^2 - 4 \div 2$ to form the objective card's number. What was the objective card?
>
> A. 1
>
> B. 3
>
> C. 4
>
> D. 10

Guy chose letter C. He said, "First 3 squared is 9. Then, 3 plus 9 is 12. Next, 12 minus 4 is 8. And 8 divided by 2 is 4." What is wrong with Guy's reasoning?

Making Generalizations

In the beginning of this unit, you learned about the Pythagorean Society. Its members used mathematics to look at the patterns in the world around them. In this section you will recognize, create and apply rules based on patterns. You will decide what might come next in a given pattern. You will also learn how to make rules from patterns and graph them.

 LESSON 3.1 ## Count on Me

 ## Start It Off

Scott was working on a "magic trick." His trick was:

Step 1: Think of a number.

Step 2: Double it.

Step 3: Add 2.

Step 4: Record your answer.

Steph said that Scott's trick was the same as hers. Her trick was:

Step 1: Think of a number.

Step 2: Add 1.

Step 3: Double it.

Step 4: Record your answer.

1. Pick a few starting numbers and try both tricks. Try whole numbers, fractions and decimals. Do both tricks have the same outcome if you start with the same number? Explain.

Minarets of Registan, Samarkand, Uzbekistan

Franklin was looking at pictures of buildings from all over the world. He saw some in Turkey and Uzbekistan that were built hundreds of years ago. The beautiful tiles that decorated the buildings fascinated him. He wondered how many tiles it would take to cover some of the walls and floors that he saw.

Franklin started with a simple tile design of triangles. He drew the pattern below.

He counted the green triangles and found there were $1 + 2 + 3 + 3 + 2 + 1$ or 12 green triangles.

His sister said that she had a faster way to count the green triangles. She added the number of green triangles on the top half and then doubled that number. She said all you had to do was simplify $2(1 + 2 + 3) = 2 \cdot 6 = 12$.

Franklin's mom said that she could find the total number of green triangles by by finding $(2 \cdot 1) + (2 \cdot 2) + (2 \cdot 3)$. The pattern that she noticed was that there were two single green triangles on the top and bottom. She also found two rows with two green triangles and two rows with three triangles in the middle.

1. a) Did Franklin's mom get the same answer as Franklin and his sister?

   b) Find another way to count the green triangles. Make sure to write out the steps of your method. Does your method also give the same answer as Franklin's?

   c) Compare your counting method to your partner's. Try to find other patterns and ways to count the triangles. Do all counting methods give you the same total?

The next tile design Franklin drew was made up of rhombuses.

This time Franklin added 5 + 4 + 3 + 4 + 5 to find the total number of tiles.

2. **a)** Regina said that she could find the total by evaluating (5 · 3) + (2 · 3). Talk to a partner about Regina's method. How does it relate to the diagram? Would she get the same answer as Franklin?

   b) Find another pattern you could use to count the rhombuses. Make sure to write the steps of your method. Does this give the same answer as Franklin's and Regina's?

   c) Compare counting methods with a partner. Try to find additional ways to count the rhombuses. Do all methods give the same answer?

For Questions 3–5, list at least two ways to count the tiles. Compare your methods with a partner's. Do you get the same totals? Did you use the same patterns?

3.

4.

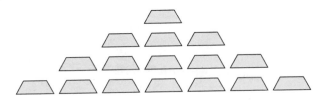

5.

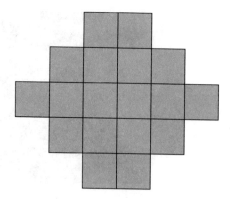

6. Tanya has made the following pattern with toothpicks.

a) Find at least three ways to count the toothpicks.
Make sure to write the steps of your method.

b) Discuss your methods with a partner. Are your counting methods equivalent to your partner's?

⬆️W rap It Up

There are often many different methods for solving a problem. Give two ways to count the toothpicks in the pattern at the right. With words and equations, show that you get the same total using either method.

Write About It

1. **a)** Give three ways to count the yellow and white squares in the pattern below.

   b) Write an equation to show each of the three ways you used to find the total. Show that the three ways are equivalent to each other.

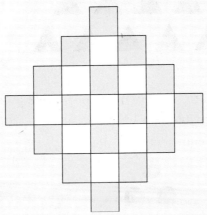

For Questions 2–4 list at least two different ways to count the tiles. Write equations for each of your methods and show that they are equal.

2.

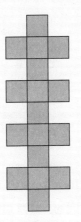

3.

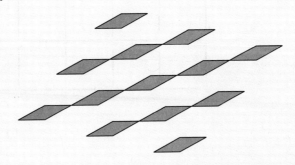

4.

5. Maury had the following marble pattern. Show at least three ways to count the marbles. Write an equation for each and show that they are equivalent.

6. Sadie said it would take 40 toothpicks to make the following pattern. She explains that there are 10 squares and it takes 4 toothpicks to make each square. Was she correct? Explain.

7. Each of the following uses 245 ÷ 18. Do they each have the same answer? Explain. Include the answer to each in your explanation.

    a) There are 245 students from W. E. B. DuBois Middle School who are going on a field trip. Each bus holds 18 students. How many buses will they need?

    b) Ms. Simpson drove 245 miles on 18 gallons of gas. To the nearest tenth of a mile, how many miles per gallon did she get?

    c) Bart's class has collected 245 pairs of socks. They are packing 18 pairs in each box. How many boxes can they fill?

8. What went wrong? Eric did the following addition: $\frac{2}{3} + \frac{3}{4} = \frac{5}{7}$. Explain what went wrong and what the sum should be.

9. Farmer McDonald had 256 hogs that had an average weight of 195 pounds.

    a) Farmer McDonald said that she had about 25 tons of hogs. Was she right? Explain.

    b) How many pounds of hogs does Farmer McDonald have? Show your work.

10. Convert each measure to the units on the right. Show your answer in fraction form and simplify all fractions.

    a) 2 quarts = _____ gallon

    b) 2 dimes = _____ dollar

    c) 24 inches = _____ yard

    d) 1,000 pounds = _____ ton

    e) 25¢ = _____ dollar

11. Which of the following is read as two thousand, four and thirty five thousandths?

    A. 2004.035   D. 2004.35

    B. 2040.035   E. 2004.0035

    C. 2000.435

LESSON 3.2 What's Next: Describing Recursive Patterns

 **Start It Off**

Jaime is at the grocery store with her mom. Her mom uses a calculator to track her spending. Jaime keeps getting answers faster than the calculator. Can you figure out how she might do that?

? Hint
See page 167

3 pounds of hamburger at $2.99 per pound = $8.97
2 gallons of milk at $3.98 per gallon = $7.96
4 packages of granola bars at $1.99 per package = $7.96
5 pounds of cheese at $4.99 each = $24.95

Use your method to figure out how much the following would cost:

1. 2 DVDs at $6.99 each

2. 3 packages of bean sprouts at $.98 each

3. 2 boxes of cereal at $2.98 per box

4. 4 containers of strawberries at $3.99 each

5. Explain your solution to one of the problems above.

Introducing Recursive Patterns

MATHEMATICALLY SPEAKING

▶ counting (natural) numbers

The Pythagoreans believed that the counting numbers {1, 2, 3, 4, 5, . . .} were the key to understanding the universe. They began by using objects like pebbles that could be touched and counted. Later, they used numerals to represent the objects they had counted.

The followers of Pythagoras might have had children like Alexandra and Dion. Alexandra and Dion loved to play games with patterns. Dion has made a pattern with stones:

Stage 1   Stage 2   Stage 3   Stage 4

1. Dion has challenged Alexandra to make the next two stages in his pattern.

   a) Sketch patterns of stones that Alexandra could make for Stages 5 and 6.

   b) Describe the pattern in words.

   c) Copy and complete the chart below.

Stage Number, n	Stones Added at this Stage	Total Number of Stones Used in Pattern, t
1		4
2	1	5
3		
4		
5		
6		
7		
8		
9		
10		

   d) You can use recursive reasoning to think about a pattern. Recursive reasoning involves thinking about how each stage in a pattern is related to the stage before it. What rule can you give for finding the number of stones in any stage if you know the number of stones used in the stage right before it?

   e) A mathematician might write a recursive rule of adding 6 at each stage as: *previous* + 6 = *new*. This means that if you take the previous number and add 6 to it, you get the new number. Write your rule for Part d as an equation using previous (p) and new (n).

Alexandra has made the following pattern with stones.

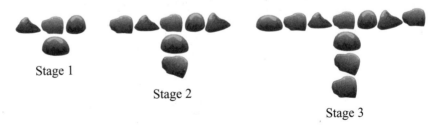

Stage 1

Stage 2

Stage 3

2. Alexandra has challenged Dion to make the next two stages in her pattern.

   a) Sketch patterns of stones that Dion could make for Stages 4 and 5.

   b) Describe your patterns in words.

c) Copy and complete the chart below.

Stage Number, n	Stones Added at this Stage	Total Number of Stones Used in Pattern, t
1		4
2	3	7
3		
4		
5		
6		
7		
8		
9		
10		

d) Write a recursive rule using words and an equation to show how the total number of stones at each stage is based on the number in the previous stage.

3. In the next game, Dion started with the following pattern. Dion has challenged Alexandra to figure out his pattern.

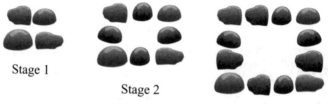

Stage 1

Stage 2

Stage 3

a) Sketch patterns of stones that Alexandra could make for Stages 4 and 5. Describe your pattern in words.

b) Write a recursive rule in words and as an equation for this pattern. How does your rule fit your pattern?

4. For each pattern below, create a chart to show the number of stones added and the number of stones used for the first ten stages. Describe the pattern you used. Write a recursive rule for the total number of stones used in each stage of the pattern.

a)

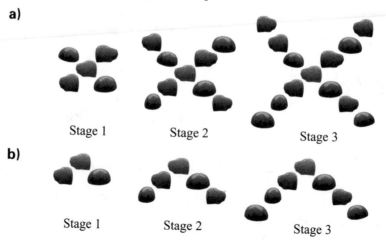

Stage 1   Stage 2   Stage 3

b)

Stage 1   Stage 2   Stage 3

5. Use small markers like counters or pennies and work with a partner to create your own stone patterns. Make a table like the one in Question 2c and write a recursive rule for your pattern.

Toothpick Patterns: More Recursive Rules

6. Kayla and Cheyenne decided to play the pattern game with toothpicks. Look at the patterns from their first two games. For the first eight stages, create a chart to show the number of new toothpicks and the total number of toothpicks used. Describe the pattern. Then write a recursive rule for the total number of toothpicks in each stage.

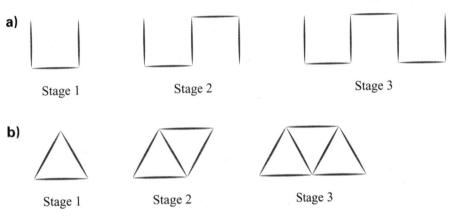

a)

Stage 1   Stage 2   Stage 3

b)

Stage 1   Stage 2   Stage 3

7. How is the pattern you described in Question 6a like the pattern you described in Question 6b? How is it different? How do the recursive rules compare? Explain.

8. Kayla made the following pattern with her toothpicks. Create a chart to show the number of new toothpicks and the total number of toothpicks used for the first ten stages. Describe your pattern. Then write a recursive rule for the total number of toothpicks in each stage.

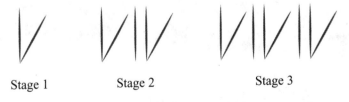

Stage 1   Stage 2   Stage 3

9. Work with a partner to create your own toothpick-pattern games. Make a table and write recursive rules for each pattern.

Recursion on a Calculator

Example

Look at Question 2. You might use a calculator to find the number of stones at stage 5. Different calculators do this differently.

Brianne said that she could use her calculator to find the patterns in Questions 1–4 above. She said that for Question 2, she put [4] into her calculator for the first stage. She then entered in [+] [3] [=] to get the second stage. Then she pressed [=] for each additional stage. To find the number of stones used in Stage 5, she pushed [4] [+] [3] [=] [=] [=] [=].

Robby tried this on his calculator, but he did not have an [=] key. Instead, his calculator had an [ENTER] key. For Stage 5 he had to push [4] [ENTER], then [+] [3] [ENTER] [ENTER] [ENTER] [ENTER].

Miranda said her calculator is a bit different. She has keys that are labeled [OP₁] and [OP₂]. To find the pattern in Question 2 she had to push [+] [3] and then [OP₁]. She then has to clear the screen. Then she puts in [4], the starting number for the pattern and pushes [OP₁] [OP₁] [OP₁] [OP₁].

---

10. Explore recursive rules on your calculator. Can you find the value for the third stage by pressing only one button after the second stage? If so, explain to a partner how to do this. Try your method on the stone patterns and toothpick patterns in this lesson. Does your method work for each of the patterns in this section?

Wrap It Up

What is a recursive rule? Use stones or toothpicks to illustrate patterns and explain how you would find a recursive rule for a given pattern.

MATHEMATICALLY SPEAKING

▶ counting (natural) numbers

▶ recursive reasoning

▶ recursive (iterative) rule

On Your Own

 **Write About It**

1. You have a pattern that starts with five stones in Stage 1. The pattern then adds two stones in each stage.

   a) Draw a pattern that fits this description.

   b) How do you find a recursive rule for the total number of stones in each stage? State it in words and with an equation.

   c) Make a table to show the first five stages of this pattern.

2. Dan decided to make his own pattern, shown below.

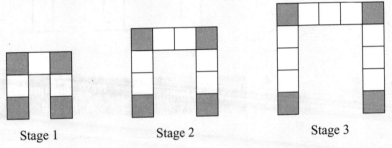

   Stage 1   Stage 2   Stage 3

   a) Draw the next two stages that could be in the pattern. Describe your pattern.

   b) Copy and complete the following chart for your pattern:

Stage Number, n	New Squares Added	Total Number of Squares at this Stage, t
1		7
2	3	10
3		
4		
5		
6		
7		
8		
9		
10		

   c) Write a recursive rule for the total number of squares at each stage. Give the rule in words and with an equation.

3. For each of the following, describe the pattern. Create a chart for the first ten stages of your pattern. Then write a recursive rule for each.

   a)

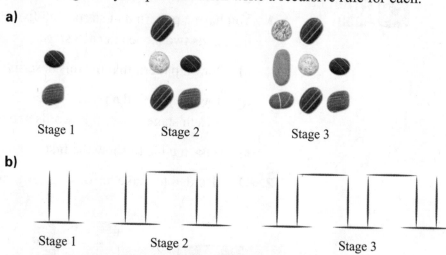

   Stage 1   Stage 2   Stage 3

   b)

   Stage 1   Stage 2   Stage 3

4.

Stage Number, n	New Toothpicks Added	Total Number of Toothpicks at this Stage, t
1		5
2	3	8
3	3	
4	3	14
5	3	

   a) Copy and complete the chart.

   b) Draw the first five stages of a toothpick pattern that fits the pattern on the chart.

   c) Write a recursive rule for the total number of toothpicks at each stage.

5. How could you use a calculator to show the total number of toothpicks at each stage rule in Question 4?

Think Beyond

6. One famous pattern is called Pascal's triangle. Pascal was a French mathematician from the 1600s. In China, the pattern is known as Yang Hui's Triangle. Yang Hui was a Chinese mathematician from the 1200s. The Persian astronomer and poet, Omar Khayyám, wrote about the pattern over 1,000 years ago. Pingale, an Indian mathematician, wrote about this pattern more than 2,200 years ago.

a) Study the triangle below and determine how it might be created. Write a rule for finding the numbers in a row based on the numbers in the row above.

b) Use your rule to create the next three rows.

c) List five interesting patterns that you notice in the triangle. Check that your patterns are true for the next three rows.

d) Search for "Pascal's triangle" online to learn about other patterns and activities.

Row 0:					1				
Row 1:				1		1			
Row 2:			1		2		1		
Row 3:		1		3		3		1	
Row 4:	1		4		6		4		1
Row 5:	1	5		10		10		5	1

Think Back

7. School starts at 8:05 each morning and ends at 3:20 pm.

   a) How long is the school day in hours and a fractional part of an hour?

   b) How long is the school day in minutes?

8. It takes Paul 15 minutes to walk from home to school at a rate of 2 miles per hour. How far does Paul live from school?

   ? Hint
   See page 167

   A. 0.25 mile   **D.** 5,280 feet

   B. 2,640 feet   **E.** None of these.

   C. $\frac{1}{4}$ mile

9. It is about 5 km from Mr. Jackson's home to school. Which of the following might be the distance?

   A. 512 meters   **D.** 51 meters

   B. 5,123 meters   **E.** None of these

   C. 51,231 meters

10. Mr. Jackson's family drinks a gallon of milk every 4 days. On average, how much milk do they drink in one day?

    A. 1 quart   **D.** 2 quarts

    B. 3 cups   **E.** None of these

    C. 3 pints

11. Paul has gotten 75%, 82% and 71% on his first three test scores.

    a) What is the mean of his first three test scores?

Think Beyond

    b) He would like to have an average (mean) of at least 80% after his fourth test. What is the minimum test score that Paul must earn on the fourth test?

LESSON 3.3 Using Explicit Rules to Describe Patterns

 Start It Off

While working with her father in his workshop, Lara found a quick way to multiply numbers by 12. Can you figure out what Lara is doing and why it works?

25 feet = _____ inches

$$25 \cdot 12 = (25 \cdot 10) + (25 \cdot 2)$$
$$= 250 + 50$$
$$= 300$$

8 feet = _____ inches

$$8 \cdot 12 = (8 \cdot 10) + (8 \cdot 2)$$
$$= 80 + 16$$
$$= 96$$

21 feet = _____ inches

$$21 \cdot 12 = (21 \cdot 10) + (21 \cdot 2)$$
$$= 210 + 42$$
$$= 252$$

Try Lara's method on each of the following:

1. 34 feet = _____ inches

2. 15 dozen pencils = _____

3. 42 feet = _____ inches

4. $12 \cdot 24 =$

5. Explain the pattern you saw. Show your solution for each of the problems above.

Mathematicians are always looking for ways to describe patterns they see in the world around them. Sometimes the patterns that mathematicians find are later used to solve everyday problems.

Writing Explicit Rules

Callie said that the recursive rules in the stone and toothpick games were easy to come up with. But she also said that using a recursive rule can be time consuming if you want to find the number of objects in a stage far along in a pattern. An **explicit rule** lets you find the number of objects in any stage without finding the number of objects in each of the stages before. In this section, you will learn to write explicit rules for pattern games.

Callie made the following pattern.

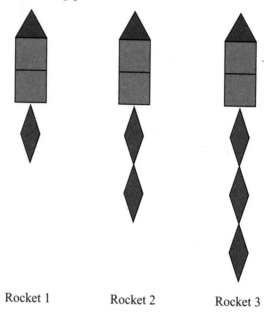

Rocket 1   Rocket 2   Rocket 3

1. Callie always used three blocks to make her rocket, but the number of blocks she used for the smoke varied. She said her pattern was to use one more block each time to make the smoke. She said that the fourth rocket would use 3 blocks for the rocket plus 4 blocks for the smoke for a total of 7 blocks.

   a) How many blocks will Callie use for the smoke in her tenth rocket? How many blocks total will Callie use in her tenth rocket?

   b) Callie said that she could write an explicit rule for the total number of blocks. She used the variable t for the total number of blocks and the variable n for the rocket number in her pattern. She wrote $t = 3 + n$. Does Callie's rule work for the number of blocks you found in Part a?

2. Callie started her next pattern like this:

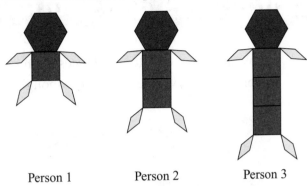

Person 1   Person 2   Person 3

a) Describe what you think Callie's pattern is. If the pattern continues, how many blocks total will Callie use for her tenth person?

b) Using your pattern, how many blocks total will Callie use for her n^{th} person?

c) Write a rule in words and an equation for the total number of blocks in any person in her pattern. In your equation, use the variable t for the total number of blocks and n for the person number.

3. For her next pattern, Callie began like this:

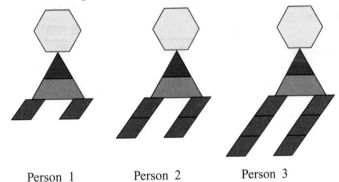

Person 1   Person 2   Person 3

a) Describe what you think Callie's pattern is this time. Using your pattern, how many blocks should Callie use in the legs of the fifth person? The tenth person?

b) Using your pattern, how many blocks total will Callie use to make the fifth person? The tenth person?

c) Write a general rule to find the number of blocks in the legs of the nth person.

d) Write a general rule to find the total number of blocks for the nth person.

Look again at the pattern of stones Dion made. The stones have been colored to help you see how Dion thought about the pattern.

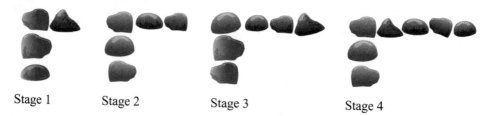

Stage 1   Stage 2   Stage 3   Stage 4

4. Alexandra said that the three stones on the left stayed the same and one was added to the right for each stage. She made this chart to show the pattern that she saw. She predicted that at Stage 7 there would be 3 + 7 or 10 stones.

Stage Number, n	Left Side plus the Rest	Total Number of Stones at this Stage, t
1	3 + 1	4
2	3 + 2	5
3	3 + 3	6
4	3 + 4	7
5		
6		
7		
8		
9		
10		

a) Copy and complete the chart. What is the recursive rule based on the way Alexandra saw the pattern?

b) Besides the three stones at the left, how many other stones will there be at Stage 21? How many total stones will there be in the pattern at Stage 21? Explain.

c) How many total stones will there be in the pattern at Stage n?

d) Describe an explicit rule for the total number of stones t at any Stage n in words.

e) Now write an equation for this explicit rule using t and n.

5. Dion said that when he looked at the pattern, he saw 2 stones at the bottom that never changed. He said the stones at the top changed by adding one more each time. He made this chart to show the pattern he saw. He predicted that at Stage 7 there would be 2 + 8 or 10 stones.

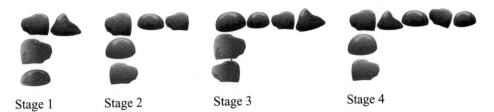

Stage 1   Stage 2   Stage 3   Stage 4

Stage Number, n	Bottom Plus Top	Total Number of Stones at this Stage, t
1	2 + 2	4
2	2 + 3	5
3	2 + 4	6
4	2 + 5	7
5		
6		
7		
8		
9		
10		

a) Copy and complete the chart. What is the recursive rule for the way Dion sees the pattern?

b) Besides the two stones at the bottom, how many stones will there be in the top row at Stage 21? How many stones will there be in the pattern at Stage 21? Explain.

c) How many stones will there be in the pattern at Stage n?

d) Describe an explicit rule for the total number of stones t at any Stage n in words.

e) Now write an equation for this explicit rule using t and n.

f) How is Dion's chart like Alexandra's? How is it different? How do their rules compare? Discuss your findings with a partner.

Look at the pattern of stones Alexandra made.

Stage 1   Stage 2   Stage 3

6. Alexandra said she saw a pattern with one stone in the middle that did not change. She said the three arms around it each grew by one stone each stage.

a)

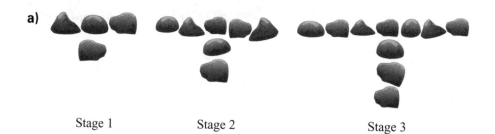

Stage 1   Stage 2   Stage 3

What is a recursive rule for this pattern?

b) Using Alexandra's pattern, how many stones will there be in the center at stage 7? How many stones will there be in each of the three arms at Stage 7?

c) Copy and complete the chart below.

Stage Number, n	Center Plus Three Arms	Total Number of Stones at this Stage, t
1	$1 + (3 \cdot 1)$	4
2	$1 + (3 \cdot 2)$	7
3	$1 + (3 \cdot 3)$	10
4		
5		
6		
7		
8		
9		
10		

d) How many total stones will there be in the pattern at Stage 21?

e) Give an explicit rule in words for the total number of stones at any given stage.

f) Write an equation for the explicit rule for the total number of stones t at any Stage n.

7. When Dion looked at Alexandra's pattern, he saw a column in the middle and two arms at the top.

Stage 1   Stage 2   Stage 3

a) What is a recursive rule for this pattern based on how Dion is looking at it?

b) Using Dion's pattern, how many stones will there be in the center column at Stage 7? How many stones will there be in each of the 2 arms at Stage 7?

c) Copy and complete the chart below.

Stage Number, n	Center Column Plus Two Arms	Total Number of Stones at this Stage, t
1	$2 + (2 \cdot 1)$	4
2	$3 + (2 \cdot 2)$	7
3	$4 + (2 \cdot 3)$	10
4		
5		
6		
7		
8		
9		
10		

d) How many total stones will there be in the pattern at Stage 21?

e) Give an explicit rule in words for the total number of stones at any given stage.

f) Write an equation for the explicit rule for the total number of stones t at any Stage n.

g) How is Dion's chart like Alexandra's? How is it different? How do their rules compare? Discuss your findings with a partner.

8. Look at Kayla's toothpick pattern.

Stage 1   Stage 2   Stage 3

a) Describe a pattern that Kayla might have seen in the toothpicks.

b) Write a recursive rule based on the pattern you described in Part a.

c) Copy and complete the table using your pattern. In the center column, include expressions that represent the pattern you described.

Stage Number, n	Your Expression	Total Number of Toothpicks at this Stage, t
1		3
2		5
3		7
4		
5		
6		
7		
8		

d) How many total toothpicks will there be in the pattern at Stage 21? Explain.

e) Give an explicit rule in words and an equation for the total number of toothpicks at any given stage.

f) Compare your answers with a partner's. How are they alike and how are they different? Do you have the same recursive rule? The same explicit rule?

9. The explicit rule "The total is equal to 2 plus 3 times the Stage number" is given by the equation $t = 2 + 3n$.

a) Draw a pattern with toothpicks that would match this rule.

b) What is the recursive rule for your pattern?

c) Make a chart to depict this pattern with the following columns: stage number, your pattern using a sum and the total number of toothpicks.

d) Compare your drawing of the toothpick pattern and your chart with a partner.

 Wrap It Up

What is the difference between an explicit rule and a recursive rule?

Draw the first four stages of a pattern with pattern blocks and explain your pattern in words. Describe the recursive rule for your pattern. Include a three-column chart for the number of blocks used in the first ten stages and give the explicit rule. Compare your patterns and rules with a partner.

On Your Own

Write
About It

1. Keri said the pattern below begins with one stone in the center. The four arms grow by 1 at each stage.

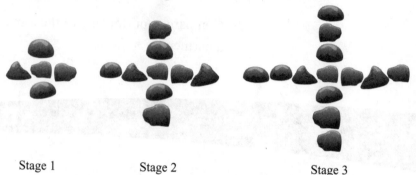

Stage 1   Stage 2   Stage 3

a) Make a three-column chart to show the first ten stages of Keri's pattern.

b) What is the recursive rule for Keri's pattern?

c) Write an explicit rule for Keri's pattern in words and with an equation.

d) Use your rule to determine the total number of stones, t, for stage n.

2. For each of the following describe a pattern that was used to create the first three stages. Write a recursive rule for the total number of stones, toothpicks or blocks. Then write an explicit rule in both words and as an equation for the total number of objects.

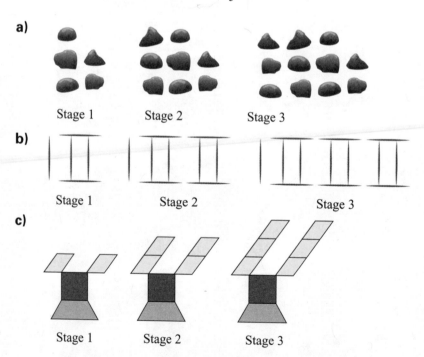

a)

Stage 1   Stage 2   Stage 3

b)

Stage 1   Stage 2   Stage 3

c)

Stage 1   Stage 2   Stage 3

3. Look at Dan's pattern of squares.

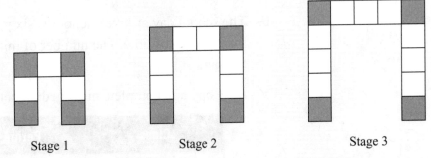

Stage 1   Stage 2   Stage 3

In his pattern the four teal squares in the corners stay the same. The white squares on the inside of each side grow by one each stage.

a) What is the recursive rule for Dan's pattern?

b) Using Dan's pattern, at Stage 7, how many teal squares will there be in the corners? How many white squares will there be? How many total squares?

c) Copy and complete the following chart using Dan's pattern:

Stage Number, *n*	Corners Plus Inside	Total Number of Squares at this Stage, *t*
1	4 + (3 · 1)	7
2	4 + (3 · 2)	10
3	4 + (3 · 3)	13
4		
5		
6		
7		
8		
9		
10		

d) Describe an explicit rule for Dan's pattern using words.

e) Write an equation for the explicit rule for the total number of squares, *t*, at any Stage *n*.

4. Jamal wrote the rule $t = 5 + 2n$.

a) Draw a pattern with stones that would match Jamal's rule.

b) Make a chart for this pattern with three columns: stage number, the expression showing your pattern and the total number of stones.

5. The school day at Jake's school is six periods long. Each period is the same length of time. The number of minutes between periods is always the same.

a) Copy and complete his schedule below.

Class	Period	Starting Time	Ending Time
Mathematics	1	7:35 am	
English	2	8:33 am	9:28 am
Physical Education	3		
Social Studies	4		
Lunch		11:27 am	11:57 am
Science	5	12:00 pm	
Chinese	6		

b) List three patterns that you notice on the chart.

Think Back

6. When Troy's bucket is one-fourth full, it has 6 cups of water in it. How much water is in Troy's bucket when it is one-eighth full?

7. Fill in the blanks:

a) $5\frac{1}{2}$ cups = _____ ounces

b) $2\frac{2}{3}$ feet = _____ inches

c) 230 cm = _____ m

d) 4.5 kg = _____ g

8. Find the average (mean) weight of 3 students who weigh 145 pounds, 92 pounds and 123 pounds.

9. Put the following in order from the shortest to the longest:

4.5 feet, 52 inches, $1\frac{1}{3}$ yards, $4\frac{1}{4}$ feet

10. Zayla has saved $18.32 toward buying a DVD of her favorite movie. The movie costs $25 with tax. How much more will she need to save?

A. $7.32

B. $7.68

C. $6.68

D. $6.78

Guess My Rule

 **Start It Off**

A.J. did the following computation:

$$
\begin{array}{r}
245 \\
\times\ 368 \\
\hline
1960 \\
14700 \\
+\ 73500 \\
\hline
90{,}160
\end{array}
$$

Use A.J.'s work and no additional computation to solve each of the following equations for n.

1. $245 \times 8 = n$

2. $14{,}700 \div n = 245$

3. $n \times 245 = 73{,}500$

4. $600 \times 245 = n$

Be prepared to explain your thinking.

Rules from Tables

Maureen and Todd like to play a game called **Guess My Rule**. In the following example, Todd has made up a secret rule using only one operation. Maureen has to guess what it is. She gives Todd an input number and Todd applies his rule and tells Maureen the output. They continue this process until Maureen thinks she knows what Todd's rule is. Maureen uses an input/output table to record her work.

1. Try to guess Todd's rule from Maureen's input/output table.

Input, i	Output, o
4	12
5	15
0	0
1	3
3	9
2	6
10	30

a) State Todd's rule in words.

b) Write an equation for Todd's rule using the variable o for the output and the variable i for the input.

Maureen said it was too easy to figure out a rule that uses only one operation. She has made up a secret rule using multiplication and addition. Todd has to guess what the rule is.

2. Todd made the following table as he tried to guess Maureen's rule.

Input, i	Output, o
0	2
1	6
2	10
3	14
4	
5	
6	

a) State in words what you think Maureen's rule might be. Make sure that the rule works for the inputs and outputs shown on the table.

b) Copy and complete the table based on your rule.

c) For your rule, what will the output be for an input of 10?

d) Write an equation for your rule to find the output o for any input number i.

Now you are going to play the game **Guess My Rule** and think like a mathematician as you look for patterns to find the secret rule.

Let's Play

GAME · · · · · · · · Guess My Rule · · · · · · · ·

Players: 2 players or teams

DIRECTIONS:

Team One: Decide on a secret rule. You may choose to use one operation or two.

Team Two: Name a number, the input and ask Team One to apply the rule.

Team One: Apply the rule to the number given by Team Two and give the result, the output.

Team Two: Record the input and output on an input/output table and name a new input number.

Team One: Give the result of applying your rule to the new number.

Team Two: Keep naming new numbers until you are ready to guess the rule. When ready, announce, "We know the rule." If correct, your score for this round is the number of input numbers. If incorrect, add five points to your score and keep guessing input numbers. If correct, add zero points to your score. Then, let Team Two pick the rule and have Team One try to guess the rule.

To Win: The team with the least number of points after five rounds is the winner.

3. This table shows the results of two teams playing **Guess My Rule**.

Input, i	Output, o
0	6
1	9
2	12
3	15
4	18

a) Guess the rule that fits the information in the table.

b) What pattern do you notice in the Input column?

c) What pattern do you notice in the Output column?

d) Does the pattern in the Output column relate to your rule? How is finding a rule for the game like finding recursive and explicit rules for pattern puzzles?

4. Here is another input/output table.

Input, i	Output, o
0	4
1	9
2	14
3	19
4	24

a) Find a rule that fits the information in the table.

b) What patterns do you notice in the Input and Output columns?

c) How do the patterns in each column relate to the recursive and explicit rules?

5. a) Make up a rule that involves multiplication and then addition.

b) Complete the chart using your rule.

Input, i	Output, o
0	
1	
2	
3	
4	

Think Beyond

c) How does your rule relate to the pattern in the Output column?

d) Does the pattern stay the same if you add first and then multiply? What if you use division or subtraction after multiplying? What if you use numbers other than whole numbers?

Wrap It Up

Imagine you are playing a **Guess My Rule** game using a rule that involves multiplication and addition. How does multiplication in your rule relate to the pattern in the Output column of the input/output table? Explain why this makes sense.

MATHEMATICALLY SPEAKING

▶ input/output table

On Your Own

 **Write About It**

1. Kim was playing **Guess My Rule** and used an explicit rule that involved multiplying the input by 4. She found that the Output column goes up by 4 each time the Input column goes up by 1. Carlos says that does not work. How would you respond? Use words and tables in your explanation.

2. Copy and complete for each input/output table and give a rule to match the table.

   a)

Input, i	Output, o
0	4
1	6
2	8
3	10
4	
5	
6	

   Using your rule, what is the output for an input of 20?

   b)

Input, i	Output, o
0	2
1	8
2	14
3	20
4	
5	
6	

   Using your rule, what is the output for an input of 20?

3. **a)** Write a rule for which the output goes up by 4 each time the input goes up by 1.

   b) Create an input/output table for your rule to show the pattern for the output.

4. **a)** Create an input/output table for the rule "multiply the number by 4 and add 5."

   b) Create an input/output table for the rule "multiply the number by 4 and add 3."

   c) How do the output numbers in the tables compare? Why?

5. **a)** Create an input/output table for the rule "multiply the number by 5 and add 5."

   b) Create an input/output table for the rule "add 1 and then multiply the result by 5."

   c) How do the output numbers in the tables compare? Why?

6. Jane made the following chart for the **Guess My Rule** game.

Input, *i*	Output, *o*
0	3
1	6
2	9
3	12
4	
5	
6	

   She guessed the rule was "multiply by 3 and then add 3." Linus said that was not right. The rule he wrote was "add 1 and then multiply by 3."

   a) Who was right?

   b) Explain what you would say to Jane and Linus about their rules.

 Think Beyond

7. **a)** Write a rule where the output goes up by 4 each time the input goes up by 2.

   b) Create an input/output table for your rule to show the pattern for the output.

   c) Graph your results by plotting points on a Cartesian coordinate system. Use the input as the *x*-coordinate and the output as the *y*-coordinate.

   d) Which variable (*x* or *y*) do you think is called the "dependent" variable? Which is called the "independent" variable? Why?

8. Use estimation to fill in the blanks.

a)
$$\begin{array}{r} 56 \\ \times\ \underline{}\,2 \\ \hline 1792 \end{array}$$

b)
$$\begin{array}{r} 72 \\ \times\ \underline{}\,8 \\ \hline 2736 \end{array}$$

c)
$$\begin{array}{r} \underline{}\,8 \\ \times\ 93 \\ \hline 2604 \end{array}$$

d) Choose one of the problems above and explain your reasoning.

9. Kiki said that $\frac{3}{5} < \frac{3}{7}$ because $5 < 7$. Explain the mistake in Kiki's reasoning.

10. Jerico bought six birthday cards at $2.45 each. She paid $0.89 in tax. She had $0.41 left after paying for the cards and the tax. How much money did she start with?

11. On a regular hexagon, all sides are the same length and all angles have the same measure. Use your protractor to measure one of the angles on this regular hexagon.

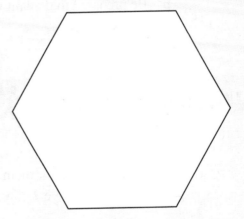

12. a) How many lines of symmetry does a regular hexagon have?

b) Sketch a regular hexagon with its lines of symmetry.

Charts and Graphs for Linear Equations

Start It Off

Paul likes to change multiplication problems to make them easier. Examine the problems below and see if you can figure out what Paul is doing.

$$5 \cdot 42 = 10 \cdot 21 \qquad 16 \cdot 50 = 8 \cdot 100 \qquad 4 \cdot 32 = 2 \cdot 64$$
$$= 210 \qquad\qquad\qquad = 800 \qquad\qquad\qquad = 128$$

Try Paul's halves and doubles method on each of the following:

1. $64 \cdot 5 =$

2. $5 \cdot 82 =$

3. $28 \cdot 5 =$

4. $50 \cdot 36 =$

5. Be prepared to explain why your solution works for the problems above.

A Fly on the Ceiling

When traders arrived at a market on the Silk Road, the hosts often had a special welcome for them. In Istanbul, this usually included tea. A host wants to have 2 cups of tea for each trader.

1. a) Copy and complete the chart to show the number of cups of tea that are needed for ten traders.

Number of Traders (n)	Number of Cups of Tea (c)
0	0
1	2
2	
3	
4	
5	
6	
7	
8	
9	
10	

b) Write a recursive rule for the number of cups of tea.

c) Write an explicit rule for the number of cups of tea for any number of traders.

Almost 400 years ago, René Descartes, a French philosopher and mathematician, devised a system for locating points in space. When Descartes was a child, he was often sick and would stay in bed until noon. He continued doing this most of his life and used this time to think about mathematics and philosophy. One of the most famous myths about Descartes is that one day while lying in bed, he watched a fly on the ceiling. He wanted to tell others about the path the fly was walking. According to the myth, this is how he invented the coordinate plane. We call the coordinate plane the Cartesian plane in his honor. As you know, the Cartesian plane is formed by drawing a vertical line and a horizontal line. These lines are called the coordinate axes. The origin is the point where the two axes meet.

On a coordinate plane, a point is located with an ordered pair of numbers (a, b). The first number, a, tells you the *x*-coordinate. This is the number of units the point is horizontally from the vertical axis. The second number, b, tells you the *y*-coordinate. This is the number of units the point is vertically from the horizontal axis. The origin is at the point $(0, 0)$.

2. How could the Cartesian plane be used to locate a fly on the ceiling?

3. On a coordinate plane like the one below, make a scatter plot of the points from your chart in Question 1. On a scatter plot, you put dots for each point you are plotting, but you do not connect the dots. Let the horizontal axis represent the number of traders, *n*. Let the vertical axis represent the number of cups of tea, *c*. In this case, you do not connect the dots because you only have whole numbers of traders and cups of tea. If the dots were connected, it would mean that you might have any fractional number of traders and cups of tea. As with all graphs, include a title, label each variable on the axes and draw the scale on each axis.

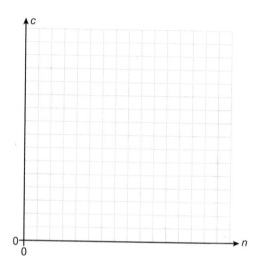

4. What pattern do you notice about the points on your scatter plot? Where is the first point on your chart? Do the points lie on the same straight line? How is this related to your chart?

5. When the traders sat down to tea, imagine that the three lead traders sat at a special head table with their hosts. The other tables can seat eight traders.

a) Copy and complete the following chart.

Number of Regular Tables, *n*	Number of Traders, *t*
0 (head table)	3
1	11
2	19
3	27
4	
5	
6	
7	
8	
9	
10	

b) Write a recursive rule for the number of traders.

c) Write an explicit rule for the number of traders for any number of regular tables. Be sure to add the three traders at the head table.

d) Make a scatter plot showing the data for the first eight regular tables. Include the three traders at the head table. Don't forget the title, axis labels and scale.

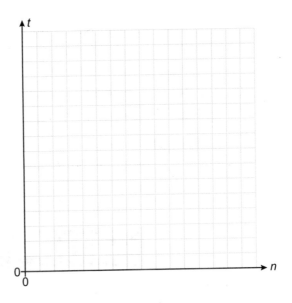

e) What pattern do you notice about the points on your scatter plot? Where on the graph is the first point from your chart?

f) If all the points on a scatter plot lie on the same line, we say that the relationship between the variables is linear relationship. Do the points on your scatter plot lie on the same line?

g) Sometimes the caravan of traders was very large. One caravan had 1,099 traders. How many regular tables would be needed if three sit at the head table and the rest sit at regular tables? How might you use the strategies of "remove" and "divide" to solve this? What if there are 4,821 traders?

h) What number of traders would fill 120 regular tables and a head table? What if there are 450 tables plus a head table? What if there are n regular tables plus a head table?

Think Beyond

i) How many regular tables are needed if there are t traders?

Businesses today use many of the same methods that were used by Silk Road traders to track profits. The algebra that was developed hundreds of years is still useful today.

The Computer Club wants to raise money for a class trip. Club members have decided to sell T-shirts with the school logo. They plan to sell them for $12 each. They have talked to two different companies about making the T-shirts. The Totally T-shirts Company will charge them $25 to set up the logo and $5 for each T-shirt. The Tees R Us Company will not charge anything to set up the logo and will charge $6 for each T-shirt.

6. **a)** Copy and complete the following chart to show the cost of buying T-shirts from each company. Include an explicit rule in the last row of the chart for the cost in dollars for any number (n) of T-shirts from each company.

Number of T-shirts, t	Totally T-shirts Total Cost, c	Tees R Us, Total Cost, c
0	$25	$0
1	$30	$6
2		
3		
4		
5		
6		
7		
8		
9		
10		
11		
12		
n		

b) Make a scatter plot of the cost of buying T-shirts from each company. Plot the number of T-shirts along the x-axis and the cost of the T-shirts along the y-axis. Put both scatter plots on the same graph. Use black dots for the points representing the T-shirts from the Totally T-shirts Company. Use red X's for the points representing the Tees R Us Company.

c) Do both companies have a point plotted at the origin? Why or why not?

d) Is there a linear relationship between the number of T-shirts and the cost for either company?

e) If the Computer Club decides to sell 20 T-shirts, should they get their T-shirts from Totally T-shirts or from Tees R Us? Explain.

f) If the Computer Club decides they can sell 50 T-shirts, should they get their T-shirts from Totally T-shirts or from Tees R Us? Explain.

g) The profit that the Computer Club will make is the amount of money received from selling T-shirts minus any costs. What will their profit be if they buy the T-shirts from Totally Tees and sell 50 T-shirts at $12 apiece? What if they buy them from Tees R Us?

h) If the Computer Club needs a profit of at least $200 for the class trip, from which company should they buy their T-shirts? How many T-shirts would they need to sell to make at least $200?

 **Wrap It Up**

How do you make a chart from an explicit rule? How do you make a scatter plot from a chart? How can you tell whether your scatter plot will have a point at the origin? How does the information on the chart compare to the information on the scatter plot? Which do you prefer? Why?

MATHEMATICALLY SPEAKING

▶ Cartesian plane (coordinate plane)

▶ coordinate plane

▶ linear (relationship)

▶ ordered pair

▶ origin (of the Cartesian plane)

▶ scatter plot

▶ *x*-coordinate

▶ *y*-coordinate

On Your Own

Write About It

1. The students in Jefferson Middle School are divided into teams of 25 for a competition. Fourteen students are acting as judges and are not on any team.

   a) Make a chart for the number of students required for 5 teams, including the students acting as judges. Begin with 0 teams and 14 students. Be sure to describe any variables you use.

   b) Plot this information on a scatter plot.

   c) Compare the scatter plot and the chart. How would you find the recursive rule from each? How would you find the explicit rule from each?

   d) Does the pattern show a linear relationship? How can you tell from the scatter plot? How could you tell from the recursive rule?

Think Beyond

   e) How might you use the information on the chart to write an explicit rule? How might you use the scatter plot for this? How might you use the explicit rule to determine whether the relationship is linear?

2. a) Make a chart to show the explicit rule $3x + 2 = y$ for any whole number x from 0 to 6.

   b) Make a scatter plot to display the information from your chart.

   c) Does your scatter plot include a point at the origin? Why or why not?

3. The Math Club is planning a Read-A-Thon to raise money to buy new calculators. Dan is going to ask sponsors for $5 each. Su plans to ask for $2 from each sponsor plus an additional $1 for each book she reads. Lora will ask each sponsor for $2 for each book she reads.

   a) Copy and complete the chart for Dan, Su and Lora.

Number of Books Read, n	Dan Money Collected from 1 Donor, a	Su Money Collected from 1 Donor, a	Lora Money Collected from 1 Donor, a
0	$5	$2	$0
1	$5	$3	$2
2			
3			
4			
5			

b) Who will collect the most money from each donor if they each read two books? Who will collect the least money? What if they each read three books? What if they each read four or more books?

c) Draw a scatter plot to show the information from your chart. Use the number of books read as the variable on the horizontal axis. Use the amount of money collected from one donor as the variable on the vertical axis. Use a different color for the scatter plot for each of the three students.

d) How much money will Lora collect if she reads four books and has three donors?

e) If you know that Dan has collected $15, do you know how many donors he has? Explain.

f) If you know that Su has collected $15, do you know how many donors she has? Explain.

g) Do you think Lora will collect $15? Explain.

h) Write a recursive rule for the amount of money collected from each donor for each of the three students.

i) Write an explicit rule for the amount of money collected from each donor based on the number of books each of the three students read.

j) Compare a chart to a scatter plot to display this information. Which do you prefer? Why?

4. Consider the following scatter plot.

a) Write a situation that could be described by the scatter plot.

b) Make a chart to show the same information. Continue the pattern for all whole numbers on the x-axis up to 10.

c) What recursive rule describes your chart and scatter plot?

d) What explicit rule describes your chart and scatter plot? What do your variables mean in your situation?

e) If this pattern continues until $x = 25$, what would the value for y be?

f) If the variable on the y-axis is 65, what is the value of the variable on the x-axis?

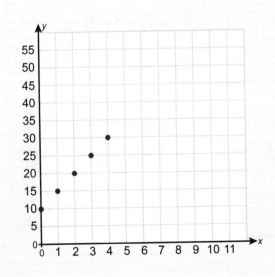

**Think
Beyond**

5. Jack is taking empty plastic milk cartons to the recycling center to earn money for the Math Club calculators. In 12 days, he collected a total of 246 empty cartons. Each day he collected three more cartons than the day before.

> **? Hint**
> See page 167

a) Make a chart to show the number of cartons he collected on each of the 12 days.

b) Make a scatter plot to show the same information.

c) Write a recursive rule to describe the number of milk cartons collected each day.

d) Write an explicit rule to describe the number of milk cartons collected each day.

**Think
Back**

6. Six bottles of water cost $3.60. At this rate, what is the cost of one bottle?

7. Morgan correctly answered 15 out of 20 questions on her last math test. What fraction of the questions were wrong?

    A. $\frac{15}{20}$ **C.** $\frac{1}{4}$

    B. $\frac{5}{15}$ **D.** $\frac{3}{4}$

8. A printer can print 300 pages in 15 minutes. At this rate, how long would it take to print 800 pages? Show your work.

9. Jeremy paid for three notebooks with a $20 bill and got $4.40 in change. What was the average cost of each notebook?

10. The length of a rectangle is three times its width. The perimeter of the rectangle is 48 cm.

a) What are the length and the width of the rectangle? Draw a sketch of the rectangle to show your solution.

b) What is the area of the rectangle?

Optional Technology Lesson for this section available in your eBook

Sum It Up

In this section you continued to think like a mathematician. You used patterns to make generalizations and then write rules and formulas. You should now understand the following:

Patterns and Generalizations

- When you see a pattern, you can often find the number of the objects in many different ways. You could count them or use variables and expressions.

- Tables, diagrams, words and symbols are used to represent, analyze and generalize patterns.

- For example: In the following design, you count the squares in the diagrams. Make a table and look for patterns.

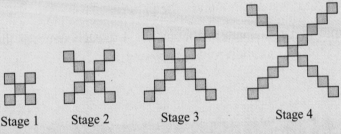

| Stage 1 | Stage 2 | Stage 3 | Stage 4 |

Table for Recursive Rule

Stage Number	New Squares Added	Total Number of Squares at this Stage
1	.	5
2	4	9
3	4	13
4	4	17

Table for Explicit Rule

Stage Number, n	Center Square Plus Four Arms	Total Number of Squares at this Stage, t
1	$1 + (4 \cdot 1)$	5
2	$1 + (4 \cdot 2)$	9
3	$1 + (4 \cdot 3)$	13
4	$1 + (4 \cdot 4)$	17
5	$1 + (4 \cdot 5)$	21
n	$1 + (4 \cdot 6)$	$t = 1 + (4 \cdot n)$

Rules for Patterns

- Rules for patterns might be expressed in words or symbols.

- Recursive rules give information about each stage based on the previous stage in a pattern. The explicit rule for a linear relationship is to multiply the x-variable by the change in each stage and add the constant amount in the pattern. Explicit rules are based on the stage number.

- If a pattern changes by the same amount in each stage, the pattern shows a linear relationship. The recursive rule is to add that change for each step.

Recursive: previous + change = new

In the example above, the recursive rule is *previous + 4 = new*.

Explicit: $x \cdot$ amount of change in each step + the constant amount.

The explicit rule for a linear relationship is to multiply the x-variable by the change in each stage and add the constant amount in the pattern.

In the example above, the pattern changes by 4 in each stage, as the 5 center squares remains constant. The explicit rule is $y = 4x + 5$.

Graphing Linear Relationships

- We use input/output tables to display a relationship input and output values for a rule. We can then graph the points from the table onto a Cartesian coordinate system.

- If the output increases by the same amount each time the input increases by 1, the relationship is linear.

- When a linear relationship is graphed on a Cartesian coordinate system, the points will lie on the same line.

For example, the scatter plot is graphed from the following input/output table. Note the points lie on the same line and so the relationship is linear. The explicit rule for this relationship is $y = 4x + 3$.

Input, x	Output, y
0	3
1	7
2	11
3	15
4	19
5	23
6	27

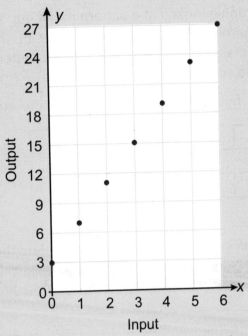

MATHEMATICALLY SPEAKING

Do you know what these mathematical terms mean?

▶ Cartesian plane (coordinate plane)

▶ coordinate

▶ coordinate plane

▶ counting (natural) numbers

▶ explicit rule

▶ input/output table

▶ linear (relationship)

▶ ordered pair

▶ origin (of the Cartesian plane)

▶ recursive reasoning

▶ recursive (iterative) rule

▶ scatter plot

▶ x-coordinate

▶ y-coordinate

Study Guide

Making Generalizations

Part 1. What did you learn?

1. Carla and Ronnie looked at a pattern made out of marbles. To count the marbles, Carla calculated $2 + 4 + 6 + 8 + 6 + 4 + 2$. Ronnie calculated $2(2 + 4 + 6) + 8$. Draw a pattern of marbles that could be counted with these methods.

2. Stages four, five and six of a pattern are pictured below.

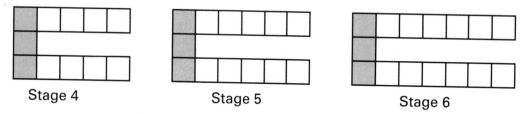

Stage 4   Stage 5   Stage 6

a. Use stages 4, 5 and 6 to copy and complete the chart.

Stage Number	Total Number of Squares Used
1	
2	
3	
4	11
5	13
6	15
7	
8	
9	
10	

b. Write a recursive rule for this pattern.

c. Write an explicit rule for this pattern.

3. Stage one of a toothpick pattern is pictured below. The recursive rule is "*Previous* + 4 = *New.*"

Stage 1

   a. Draw what stages two, three and four might look like.

   b. Describe the pattern in words.

   c. Write an explicit rule that could be used to find *t*, the total number of toothpicks, in any stage number, *n*.

4. Create an Input/Output table for "multiply by 5 and add 4."

Input	Output
0	
1	
2	
3	
4	
5	

5. Finn made figures using pattern blocks. These are the first three figures he made.

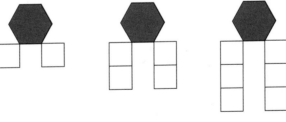

Stage 1   Stage 2   Stage 3

a. Find a pattern that describes how Finn's figures are growing. Then, use your pattern to copy and complete the table below.

Stage Number	Total Number of Patterns Blocks
1	
2	
3	7
4	
5	
10	

b. Based on your pattern, how many squares will he use for the 11ᵗʰ figure?

c. Based on your pattern, how many total blocks will he use for the 11ᵗʰ figure?

d. Based on your pattern, how many squares will he use for the nth figure?

e. Based on your pattern, how many total blocks will he use for the nth figure?

6. Dan and Pete were playing Guess My Rule. Instead of using a chart, they used a graph. Pete was trying to guess Dan's rule using the graph to the right.

a. Use the graph to create an Input/ Output table.

b. What might Dan's rule have been?

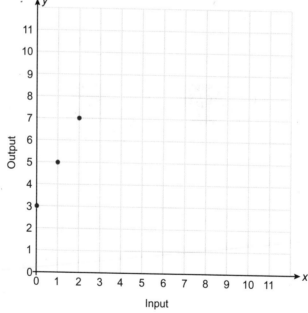

7. This month, Abby, Tucker, Zula and Nalesh are participating in a recycle-a-thon. Each student has a different pledge plan that represents the total number of dollars, t, they will earn from a sponsor if they recycle n cans during the month. Match each description with the correct recursive rule and the correct explicit rule of each plan.

a. Abby's Plan: A flat donation of $2 plus fifty cents for each can I recycle.

e. *Previous* + 1 = *New*

i. $2n + 1 = t$

b. Tucker's Plan: A flat donation of $2 plus $1 for each can I recycle.

f. *Previous* + 2 = *New*

j. $2.5n = t$

c. Zula's Plan: A flat donation of $1 plus $2 for each can I recycle.

g. *Previous* + $\frac{1}{2}$ = *New*

k. $n + 2 = t$

d. Nalesh's Plan: A donation of $2.50 for each can I recycle.

h. *Previous* + 2.5 = *New*

l. $0.5n + 2 = t$

8. Find a rule that fits the values in the chart. Then, use your rule to copy complete the table.

What is the rule?

Input	Output
1	6
2	13
3	20
4	27
5	34
	55
9	
13	90
30	
20	139

9. Theo looked at the first three stages of the pattern below. He said, "The explicit rule is add two to the stage number to get the total number of blocks." He wrote this as $n + 2 = t$, where n is the stage number and t is the total number of blocks. His friend Jada said his rule would not work since stage 3 does not have 5 squares. What is wrong with Theo's reasoning?

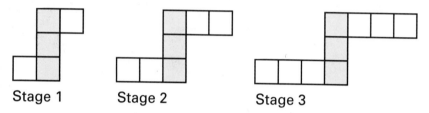

Stage 1   Stage 2   Stage 3

10. Sasha and Nikki are partners in math class. Sasha showed Nikki the table below. Instead of giving her the output values, she said, "The recursive rule is add four." Use the recursive rule to fill in the output values. Nikki said that that was not enough information to fill in the chart. Is Nikki right? Why or why not?

Input	Output
0	
1	
2	
3	
4	
5	

Unit Study Guide

A Balancing Act: Focusing on Equality, Algebraic Expressions and Equations

Part 1. What did you learn?

SECTION 1

1. Copy and complete the following paragraph. Use the words listed under "Mathematically Speaking" at the end of Section 1.

    Maria's teacher asked her to _____ the
    __1__
    _____ 58 + (x + 42) for x = 34. Maria used the
    __2__
    _____ property of _____ to create the
    __3__   __4__
    _____ expression 58 + (42 + x). Then she used
    __5__
    the _____ property of _____ to create
    __6__   __7__
    (58 + 42) + x. She added to find that the _____
    __8__
    was _____ to 134.
    __9__

2. Examine the balance scale below.

    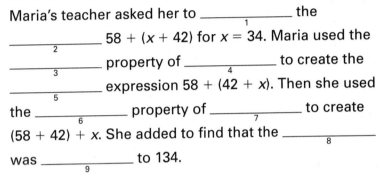

    | | | | |
    | A | C | B | D |
    | 18 lbs | 22 lbs | 14 lbs | ? |

    a. If box A weighs 18 pounds, box B weighs 14 pounds, box C weighs 22 pounds, how much does box D weigh?

    b. Use a bar diagram to represent and solve this problem.

3. Use a bar diagram to find n in the equation $643 + 60 = 640 + n$.

4. Hamed filled six bags with the same number of bananas in each bag. After he filled the bags, he had two loose bananas. Is it possible that Hamed had a total of 34 bananas? Why or why not?

5. Hamed placed the same number of pears in each of 4 bags. He wrote the equation $4p + 3 = 51$.

    a. What does the equation $4p + 3 = 51$ tell you about the total number of pears Hamed had?

    b. Use a bar diagram to figure out the number of pears in each bag.

6. Are the expressions $4x + 8$ and $12x$ ever the same? Why or why not?

7. Evaluate each of the following expressions for $n = 4$ and $b = 7$.

a. $3n + 2 + b$

b. $10b + 25 + n + 1$

8. Nina evaluated the expression $6a + 3$ for a certain value of a. She wrote $18 + 3 = 21$. What was the value of a Nina used to evaluate the expression?

SECTION 2

9. Use symbols to show each step in the number trick below. Compare your final answer with a partner. What do you notice?

Step 1	Choose a two-digit number.	
Step 2	Triple your number.	
Step 3	Add seven.	
Step 4	Subtract three times your original number.	
Step 5	Subtract five.	
Step 6	Record your final answer.	

10. Use inverse operations and backtracking to find the original number. Show your work.

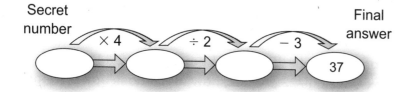

11. Aisha has both crayons and markers in her art case. The following two equations describe c the number of crayons and m number of markers she has.

$$c + m = 30$$
$$c = 4m$$

a. Use words to compare the number of crayons and markers Aisha has.

b. Find the number of crayons and the number of markers Aisha has. Show or explain how you got your answer.

12. Insert parentheses into the expression $10 - 3 \cdot 12 \div 2 + 4$ to create 3 non-equivalent expressions. Evaluate each expression.

13. Evaluate each of the following expressions. Remember the order of operations.

   a. $12 - 3^2 + 6 \cdot 5 - 2$

   b. $84 + 4^2 - 5 \cdot (13 - 4 + 1)$

   c. $3 + 2 \cdot (5^2 - 5)$

14. Imagine you dealt the following five cards while playing Krypto: 2, 3, 6, 9 and 10.

   a. Use at least 3 of the 5 cards to make an expression that is equivalent to 2.

   b. Use at least 3 of the 5 cards to make an expression that is equivalent to 8.

   c. Use an exponent to write another expression for Part a or b.

15. Julie bought one package of sunflower seeds and one package of geranium seeds to plant in her garden. The package of sunflower seeds costs $0.90 more than the package of geranium seeds. Both packages cost a total of $2.60.

   a. What does g stand for in the bar diagram below?

   b. What does the expression "$g + 0.90$" represent in the problem?

   c. Use the bar diagram below to find the price of each package of seeds.

g	g	$+ 0.90$
2.60		

16. Ben's band conductor told the students that they should practice at least 60 minutes each day. If m stands for number of minutes the students should practice, choose the inequality that represents this statement.

   $m < 60$ $\qquad$ $m > 60$ $\qquad$ $m \geq 60$ $\qquad$ $m \leq 60$

17. Jerry's dog just had a litter of puppies. Each puppy was no more than 12 inches long. If *n* stands for the length of a puppy in inches, choose the inequality that represents this statement.

$n > 12$ $\qquad$ $n < 12$ $\qquad$ $n \geq 12$ $\qquad$ $n \leq 12$

SECTION 3

18. Copy and complete the following paragraph. Use the words listed under Mathematically Speaking at the end of Section 3.

Jose created the _____ table and the _____
₁ ₂
_____ pictured below. Each point on the graph and each
₃
row in the table is represented by an _____ pair. For
₄
example, the _____ located at (0, 1) on the graph appears
₅
as the first row of the table. A _____ rule for his table is
₆
"add 5." An _____ rule for his table is *Input* × 5 + 1 =
₇
Output. The relationship between the input and output values is

_____ since the points lie on the same line.
₈

Input, x	Output, y
0	1
1	6
2	11
3	16
4	21
5	26

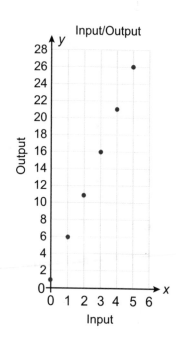

19. At the Pembroke Town carnival, admission is free but each ride costs $2.00.

a. Use the information given to copy and complete the following chart.

Number of Rides	Total Dollars Spent at the Carnival
0	0
1	
2	
3	
4	
5	

b. Write a recursive rule for the increase in the amount of money spent as the number of rides increases by 1.

c. Write an explicit rule for the cost, c, of any number of rides, r.

d. Make a scatter plot for the relationship between number of rides and total cost. Don't forget the title and axis labels.

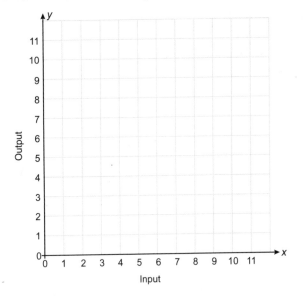

e. Is the relationship between the number of rides and the cost linear?

20. The Hingham Town carnival has a flat admission fee of $3.00 and each ride costs $1.00.

a. Use the information given to fill in the following chart.

Number of Rides	Total Dollars Spent at the Carnival
0	3
1	
2	
3	
4	
5	

b. Write a recursive rule for the increase in the amount of money spent at the carnival as the number of rides increases by 1.

c. Write an explicit rule for the cost, c, of any number of rides, r.

d. Make a scatter plot for the relationship between number of rides and cost. Don't forget the title, axis labels and scale.

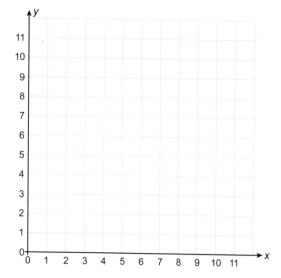

e. Compare and contrast the table and graph from Question 19 to the table and graph from Question 20. How are they similar? How are they different?

21. Find a rule that fits the values and complete each chart.

a.

Input	Output
0	4
1	8
2	12
3	
10	
32	

b.

Input	Output
0	1
1	6
2	11
3	16
7	
10	
100	

22. Examine the toothpick pattern below.

| Stage 1 | Stage 2 | Stage 3 |

a. Describe the pattern in words.

b. Use your description from Part a to copy and complete the chart below.

Stage Number	Total Number of Toothpicks Used
1	
2	
3	
4	
5	

c. Write a recursive rule for your pattern.

d. Write an explicit rule that could be used to find *t*, the total number of toothpicks, in any stage number, *n*.

23. Neil is participating in the Math Club's Read-a-thon. If he reads 0 books, each sponsor will owe him $2. If he reads 1 book, each sponsor will owe him a total of $3. If he reads 4 books, each sponsor will owe him a total of $6. Each sponsor will pay Neil the same amount for each book he reads. Neil created a scatter plot of this data.

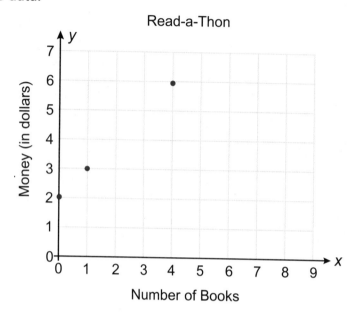

Read-a-Thon

Number of Books

a. Copy the table below. Then use the scatter plot to complete the table.

Number of Books	Total Money Donated
0	
1	
2	
3	
4	
5	

b. Write a recursive rule for Neil's plan.

c. Write an explicit rule for Neil's plan. Be sure to define your variables.

24. Althea thinks that the sentence, "There are twice as many ducks as horses" should be written as "$2d = h$, where d stands for the number of ducks and h stands for the number of horses." Bob thinks it should be written as "$2h = d$." What do you think? Which equation is the correct interpretation of the sentence?

25. Dana and Linda were playing Krypto. The five cards dealt were 1, 2, 3, 2 and 6 and the objective card was 6. Dana wrote $2 + 2 \times 3 - 6$. Linda told her that this would not equal 6. Is Linda right? Why or why not?

26. Blair said that the explicit rule for the Input/Output table below is Input + 3 = Output since "we add three each time." Her friend Tomas disagrees but is having difficulty explaining why. What might Tomas say or do to convince Blair of her error? Include the correct rule in your explanation.

Input	Output
1	5
2	8
3	11
4	13

27. Tracy tried to solve the following problem:

> Jill and Rick own a total of 20 horses and chickens. They own 4 more chickens than horses. How many chickens do they own? How many horses?

Here is a picture of her bar diagram.

4	h
20	

Tracy used her bar diagram to write and solve this equation:

$4 + h = 20$

$h = 16$

Then, she wrote, "They own 16 horses and 4 chickens."

Where did Tracy go wrong? How could you help her?

associative property of addition The mathematical rule that states that changing the grouping of addends does not change their sum.

Example:
For numbers a, b, and c: $a + (b + c) = (a + b) + c$.
$3 + (7 + 4) = (3 + 7) + 4$

associative property of multiplication The mathematical rule that states that changing the grouping of factors does not change their product.

Example:
For numbers a, b, and c: $a \cdot (b \cdot c) = (a \cdot b) \cdot c$.
$3 \cdot (6 \cdot 10) = (3 \cdot 6) \cdot 10$

bar diagram A diagram using bars of equal length to represent equal expressions or quantities.

Example:

$4 (79) + t = 475$

79	79	79	79	t
475				

base The factor of a repeated multiplication when expressed in exponential form. In an exponential expression of the form x^y, x is the base.

Example:
$2 \cdot 2 \cdot 2 = 2^3$ 2 is the base
$5 \cdot 5 = 5^2$ 5 is the base

commutative property of addition The mathematical rule that states that changing the order of addends does not change their sum.

Example:
For numbers a and b: $a + b = b + a$.
$4 + 6 = 6 + 4$

commutative property of multiplication The mathematical rule that states that changing the order of factors does not change their product.

Example:
For numbers a and b: $a \cdot b = b \cdot a$.
$4 \cdot 7 = 7 \cdot 4$

constant A value that does not vary.

Example:
In the expression $x + 3$, 3 is a constant.
In the formula $A = \pi r^2$, π is a constant.

convention A widely used rule, method, or practice established by usage or custom.

coordinate Each number in an ordered pair that gives a point's location on a Cartesian (coordinate) plane.

Example:
The ordered pair (2, 3) has an x-coordinate of 2 and a y-coordinate of 3.

coordinate plane (Cartesian plane) A plane formed by two number lines, called axes, intersecting at a right angle at each number line's 0 points. This allows pairs of numerical values (coordinates) to represent any location on the plane.

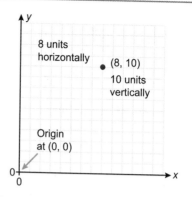

counting (natural) numbers The set of numbers used to count; the set of positive integers {1, 2, 3, 4, ...}.

equal The relationship of two numbers, expressions or terms that have the same value, as signified by an equal sign.

Example:
3 + 2 and 5 both have a value of 5 and therefore 3 + 2 = 5.

2(0.25 + 3) and 0.5 + 6 both have a value of 6.5 and therefore 2(0.25 + 3) = 0.5 + 6.

equation A mathematical sentence stating that two expressions are equal.

Example:

$$\left(\tfrac{1}{a}\right)(a) = 1$$

$$3x + 4 = 7$$

equivalent Equal in value; different representations of the same thing.

Example:

$\frac{1}{2}$ and 0.5 are equivalent.

$\frac{2}{3}$ and $\frac{6}{9}$ are equivalent.

equivalent expressions Expressions that simplify to an equal value for all values of the variable(s) they contain.

Example:
$l + l + w + w$ and $2l + 2w$ are equivalent expressions for the perimeter of a rectangle.

evaluate (an expression) To substitute numerical value(s) for a variable (or variables) in an expression, and then carry out the operations in the correct order resulting in a single numerical value.

Example:
Evaluate: $3(x + y) + 2\,(10)$ for $x = 2$ and $y = 3$:

$$3(2 + 3) + 2\,(10) =$$

$$3(5) + 20 =$$

$$15 + 20 = 35$$

explicit rule A rule that provides an output value directly from the application of the rule on an input value.

Example:

For a circle of radius r, the area A is given by the explicit rule $A = \pi r^2$.

The number of bricks b in a walkway made up of s sections is given by the explicit rule of $b = 8s + 4$.

---

exponent In an exponential expression, the raised number or expression indicating the number of times a number or expression is used as a factor in repeated multiplication. In an exponential expression of the form x^y, x is the base.

Example:

$2 \cdot 2 \cdot 2 = 2^3$ The exponent is 3.

$(3r)(3r) = (3r)^2$ The exponent is 2.

---

expression A mathematical phrase made of a combination of numbers, variables and/or operations.

Example:

$5x + 2$

πr^2

$3 + 4\,(5 - 2)$

---

flowchart A graphic representation showing the sequence of steps of an activity. In mathematics, it can represent the correct order of operations for simplifying or evaluating an expression or equation.

Example:

Evaluate $2 \cdot 3 + 5$.

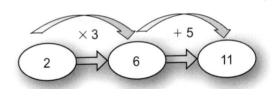

---

inequality A statement containing the symbols $>$ (greater than), $<$ (less than), $\geq$ (greater than or equal to), $\leq$ (less than or equal to), or $\neq$ (not equal to) to indicate how one quantity relates to another.

Example:

$5 > 2$

$3 < 7$

The value of any 3 coins $\geq$ 3 cents.

---

input/output table A table that pairs the input values of a rule with the corresponding output values.

Example:

Rule: $y = 2x + 5$

Table:

Input (x)	Output (y)
0	5
0.5	6
3	11

---

inverse operations Pairs of operations that undo each other.

Example:

Addition and Subtraction: $5 + 2 = 7$ $7 - 2 = 5$

Multiplication and Division: $5 \cdot 3 = 15$ $\frac{15}{3} = 5$

like terms Terms in an expression or equation that include the same variable(s), each raised to the same power(s); like terms can be combined to simplify expressions and equations.

Example:

In the expression $3 + 4x + 6 + 7x$, 3 and 6 are like terms, and $4x$ and $7x$ are like terms. Since $3 + 6 = 9$ and $4x + 7x = 11x$, we can simplify $3 + 4x + 6 + 7x$ as $9 + 11x$.

---

linear (relationship) A relationship between two variables whose ordered pairs form a straight line when graphed. The recursive rule for a linear relationship shows addition or subtraction of a constant at each step.

Example:

Graph:

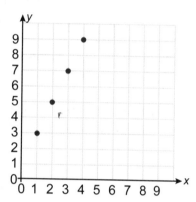

Recursive: $New = Previous + 2$

---

order of operations The prescribed order for evaluating expressions and solving equations:
1) perform all operations within parentheses;
2) simplify all numbers with exponents;
3) multiply and divide in order from left to right;
4) add and subtract in order from left to right.

---

ordered pair A pair of numbers in which order matters.

Example:

On a coordinate plane with an x-axis and y-axis, the ordered pair $(8, 10)$ indicates a point located a distance of 8 units horizontally from the y-axis and 10 units vertically from the x-axis.

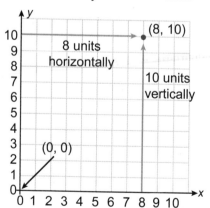

origin (of the Cartesian plane) The point of intersection of the axes of the coordinate plane; the point represented by the coordinate pair (0, 0).

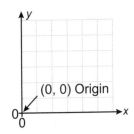

recursive (iterative) rule A rule that is applied to the result of a previous application of itself; the input is a previous output of the rule.

Example:

Every day I save 25 cents of my lunch money and put it in a jar on my desk. Each day I can express the amount of money I have using the recursive rule. *New = Previous + 25.*

recursive reasoning A type of reasoning used to find a repetitive pattern in which each term is based on a previous term in the pattern.

scatter plot The graph of a set of ordered pairs on a coordinate plane.

Example:

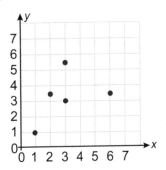

solution A number or set of numbers that produces a true statement when substituted for a variable (or variables) in a mathematical sentence, such as an equation or inequality; the answer to a mathematical problem.

Example:

Equation: $5x = 10$ Solution: $x = 2$

Inequality: $3x > 15$ Solution: $x > 5$

solve (an equation) To find a solution to an equation. ~~nay~~

Example:
Equation

$x + 4 = 7$

$x + 4 - 4 = 7 - 4$

Solution: $x = 3$

symbol "$>$" Greater than.

Example:

$5 > 2$

$(10 + n) > 10$, where n is a positive number

symbol "≥" Greater than or equal to.

Example:

If John's height ≥ 72 inches, then John is 72 inches tall or taller.

The number of coins that sum to $1.00 is ≥ 1.

---

symbol "<" Less than.

Example:

$2 < 7$

If $x + 2 < 5$, then $x < 3$.

---

symbol "≤" Less than or equal to.

Example:

If Jessica's age ≤ 12, then Jessica is 12 years old or younger.

The amount of cereal in a 14-ounce box ≤ 14 ounces.

---

symbol "≠" Not equal to.

Example:

$4 ≠ 6$

The number of wheels on a bicycle ≠ 3.

---

variable A letter or other symbol used to represent a number or set of numbers in an expression or an equation.

Example:

$10x = 50$ The variable is x.

$5p + 3 > 20$ The variable is p.

$3\triangle + 5 > 7\square$ The variables are $\triangle$ and $\square$.

---

x-coordinate The first value in a coordinate pair; the position of a point relative to the vertical axis.

Example:

The point (3, 2) is 3 units to the right of the vertical axis.

The point (−1, −5) is 1 unit to the left of the vertical axis.

---

y-coordinate The second value in a coordinate pair; the position of a point relative to the horizontal axis.

Example:

The point (3, 2) is 2 units above the horizontal axis.

The point (−1, −5) is 5 units below the horizontal axis.

Lesson 1.3

Let's Trade
Page 24, Question 5: What if there are three bananas in each bag? What if there are five bananas in each bag?

Lesson 1.4

Equivalent Expressions
Page 34, Question 6a: Don't forget zero is a whole number and one is often important.

Lesson 2.1

On Your Own
Page 53, Question 3: Choose a number and try it.

Lesson 2.2

To Market, To Market
Page 58, Question 3: One of your equations should use addition and one should use subtraction.

Lesson 2.3

Order of Operations
Page 67, Question 1: Which student worked from left to right? Which student multiplied first, then added, then subtracted? Which student multiplied first, then subtracted, then added? Which student subtracted first, then added, then multiplied?

On Your Own
Page 76, Question 11: Did you try 1 and 2 for *a* and *b*? How about 1 and 3?

Lesson 2.5

Understanding Inequality
Page 83, Question 2b: Remember that 1 pound is 16 ounces.

Page 83, Question 2c: Remember that 1 kilogram is equal to 1,000 grams.

Put It Together
Page 86, Question 9: Put in some values for *A* and *B* that make the sentences true.

Lesson 3.2

Start It Off
Page 106: Jaime is a whiz at rounding numbers.

On Your Own, Think Back
Page 114, Question 8: How many feet are there in a mile?

Lesson 3.5

On Your Own, Think Beyond
Page 142, Question 5: Try "guess, test and refine"

Index

A

algebra   21, 22
Al-Khwarizmi, Mohammed   21
associative property
   of addition   21, 34, 36
   of multiplication   21, 36, 45

B

balance scale   2–7, 14, 16–18, 23, 39, 83, 84
bar diagram   15, 16, 39, 77–79, 93
base   70

C

Cartesian plane   135, 145. See also *coordinate plane.*
commutative property
   of addition   12, 34, 36
   of multiplication   12, 36, 45
constant   33, 34, 40
convention   68
coordinate plane   135, 145
counting (methods)   100–102
counting (natural) numbers   106

D

distributive property   115
division   57, 67, 70, 82

E

equal   2, 39, 82
equality   2, 39, 82. See also *symbols.*
equation   13, 40, 41
  constant in   33, 34, 40
  linear   137–139, 145
  solution   14
  solving
     using balance   13, 14, 16, 23, 39, 83, 84
     using bar diagram   15, 16, 77–79, 93
     using inverse operations   51, 59
     using substitution   60, 61
     symbolically   58, 59

variable in   13–16, 24, 93
with 2 variables   59–62, 93
write an   23–25, 39, 58–61, 78, 79, 83–85, 116–122, 128
equivalent expressions   34–36
explicit rule   116, 118–123, 135, 137–139, 143, 144
exponent   70, 71, 94
expression   13, 21, 40, 41. See also *equivalent expressions.*
  evaluate an   22–26, 34–36, 40, 41, 69, 70–72
  evaluate with calculator   68, 70
  write an   24, 32–34

F

fact family   32
factors   1, 12
flow charts   49–51, 92

G

games
  Guess My Rule   127–130
  Krypto   72, 73, 75
generalization   117–119, 143
Guess My Rule   127–130

H

Hypatia   76

I

inequality   82, 83, 94. See also *symbols.*
  write an   83–85
input/output tables   128–130, 144, 145
inverse operations   51, 59, 92

K

Krypto   72, 73, 75